Maths

The 11+ Study Book
and Parents' Guide

This book contains two pull-out sections:

A **Benchmark Test** at the front
A **Parents' Guide to 11+ Maths** at the back

Practise • Prepare • Pass
Everything your child needs for 11+ success

1. $7 - 4.7 =$ (_____)

2. Round 12 853 to the nearest 1000.
    a 12 000   **b** 12 900   **c** 12 850   **d** 13 000   **e** 10 000   (_____)

3. Which of these numbers has 8 and 6 as factors?
    a 48   **b** 36   **c** 42   **d** 32   **e** 56   (_____)

4. Jason wrote down the number of siblings each person in his class had.

    0, 1, 3, 4, 3, 2, 3, 4, 0, 1, 2, 3, 0

    What is the modal number of siblings? (_____)

5. Which of these shapes is the same as shape **m**?

        m   **a**   **b**   **c**   **d**   **e**   (_____)

6. Each side of a regular hexagon is 17 cm long.
    What is the perimeter of the hexagon? (_____ cm)

7. Which number could x represent?
    a 3   **b** 12   **c** 4   **d** 13   **e** 10 (_____)

    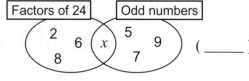

8. Phil has a jug which holds 1200 ml of water. He fills twenty-four
    10 ml test tubes from the jug. How much water is left in the jug? (_____ ml)

9. Jacques has a hexagonal spinner. What is the
    probability that it will land on a 3 or less?
    a $\frac{1}{4}$ **b** $\frac{1}{6}$ **c** $\frac{1}{3}$ **d** $\frac{1}{2}$ **e** $\frac{5}{6}$ (_____)

    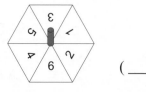

10. It takes 30 seconds to pump 20 litres of petrol into a car.
    How long would it take to pump 60 litres into a car?
    a 1 minute and 45 seconds   **c** 1 minute and 50 seconds   **e** 3 minutes
    b 1 minute and 30 seconds   **d** 2 minutes and 30 seconds   (_____)

11. $(5 + 72) \div 7 =$ (_____)

12. If $a = 6$ and $b = 4$, what is $4a + 5b$? (_____)

    END OF TEST   /12

1. $234 + 58 =$ (_____)

2.   Which pair of numbers are both multiples of 9?
     a 63 and 56   **b** 78 and 92   **c** 54 and 66   **d** 45 and 72   **e** 81 and 68   (_____)

3.   23,   18,   13,   8,   ____
     What is the next number in the sequence?
     a 2   **b** 3   **c** 1   **d** 0   **e** 4   (_____)

4. $84 \div 6 =$ (_____)

5.   What is $^{6}/_{10}$ as a decimal?
     a 0.6   **b** 0.66   **c** 0.06   **d** 0.3   **e** 0.16   (_____)

6. $87 \times 4 =$ (_____)

7.   How many right angles does this shape have?   (_____)

8.   Olga ran a race which was 25 000 m.
     How many kilometres did she run?
     a 2.5 km   **b** 0.25 km   **c** 250 km   **d** 25 km   **e** 0.025 km   (_____)

9.   Andy is measuring the width of a table. He works out that the width of the
     table is equal to the length of eight 15 cm rulers. How wide is the table?   (_____ cm)

10. Class 4H went to the zoo and counted
     how many of each animal there were.

     They recorded their results in a bar chart.
     How many giraffes and lions were there
     altogether?   (_____)

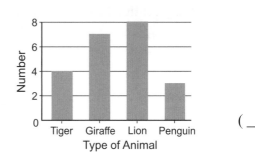

11. $^{1}/_{3}$ of hexagon **m** is shaded. Which of these
     hexagons has the same amount shaded?

     m   **a**   **b**   **c**   **d**   **e**   (_____)

12. Jeanne arrives at hockey training at 5:35 pm. She plays hockey for 90 minutes.
     At what time does she finish playing hockey?
     a 6:55 pm   **b** 7:05 pm   **c** 7:15 pm   **d** 7:25 pm   **e** 7:45 pm   (_____)

                                                                                      /12

11+ Maths — Benchmark Test

There are 36 questions in this test and it should take about 40 minutes. Write the answer to each question in the brackets at the end of the line. If there are a range of options, write the letter of the answer you have chosen. Use rough paper for your working.

Section One

1. 30 + 90 =   (_____)

2. 110 – 60 =   (_____)

3. 9 × 7 =   (_____)

4. Round 544 to the nearest 10.
    a 540   **b** 550   **c** 600   **d** 500   **e** 545   (_____)

5. What fraction of this shape is shaded?
    a ¾   **b** ⅕   **c** ¼   **d** ⅓   **e** ⅙   (_____)

6. 2, 6, 10, 14, ____
    What is the next number in the sequence?   (_____)

7. How many faces does this shape have?
    a 3   **b** 4   **c** 5   **d** 6   **e** 7   (_____)

8. How many centimetres are there in 3 metres?
    a 100   **b** 30   **c** 130   **d** 300   **e** 3000   (_____)

9. A box contains 72 bananas. The bananas are shared equally
    between 6 people. How many bananas does each person get?   (_____)

10. Which of these clocks shows a quarter to 8?

        a   **b**   **c**   **d**   **e**   (_____)

11. Emmy feeds her dog 200 g of dog food each day.
    How much food would she give her dog in 4 days?   (_____ g)

12. Simon has 87 flowers in his garden. Simon's flowers are either
    red, blue or yellow. He has 29 red flowers and 34 blue flowers.
    How many yellow flowers does he have?   (_____)

/12

Maths

The 11+ Study Book
and Parents' Guide

Practise • Prepare • Pass

Everything your child needs for 11+ success

CONTENTS

Section Four — Data Handling

Section Five — Shape and Space

Section Six — Units and Measures

Section Seven — Mixed Problems

Published by CGP

Editors:
Luke Antieul, Joe Brazier, David Broadbent, Sharon Keeley-Holden, Sarah Williams

With thanks to Luke Von Kotze, Rachel Murray, Rachel Patterson and Izabela Underwood for the proofreading.

ISBN: 978 1 84762 824 4
Website: www.cgpbooks.co.uk
Printed by Elanders Ltd, Newcastle upon Tyne.
Clipart from CorelDRAW®

Based on the classic CGP style created by Richard Parsons.

What's in the 11+

Make sure you've got your head around the basics of the 11+ before you begin.

The **11+** *is an* **Admissions Test**

1) The 11+ is a test used by <u>some schools</u> to help with their <u>selection process</u>.

2) You'll usually take it when you're in <u>Year 6</u>, at some point during the <u>autumn term</u>.

3) Schools <u>use the results</u> to decide who to accept. They might also use <u>other things</u> to help make up their mind, like information about <u>where you live</u>.

If you're unsure, ask your parents to check when you'll be taking your 11+ tests.

Some Schools *test a* **Mixture** *of* **Subjects**

1) Depending on the <u>school</u>, the 11+ can be a test on <u>different subjects</u>.

2) There are <u>four</u> main subjects that can be tested in the 11+, so you might sit papers on <u>some</u> or <u>all</u> of these:

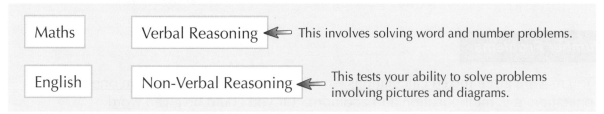

| Maths | Verbal Reasoning | ← This involves solving word and number problems. |
| English | Non-Verbal Reasoning | ← This tests your ability to solve problems involving pictures and diagrams. |

3) This book will help you with the <u>Maths</u> part of the test.

Get to **Know** *what* **Kind** *of* **Paper** *you're taking*

Your paper will either be <u>multiple-choice</u> or <u>standard answer</u>.

Multiple-Choice

1) For each question you'll be given some <u>options</u> on a <u>separate answer sheet</u>.

2) You'll need to mark your answer with a clear pencil <u>line</u> in the box next to the <u>option</u> that you think is <u>correct</u>.

Look out for the 'Tips and Tricks' boxes in this Study Book — they'll give you practical advice about the test.

Standard Answer

1) You'll be expected to <u>write down</u> the correct answer for some questions, but you may have some <u>options</u> to choose from for others.

2) You'll usually <u>mark</u> or <u>write</u> your answer on the <u>question paper</u>.

Check which type of <u>question paper</u> you'll be taking, so you know what it <u>looks</u> like and <u>where</u> your answers go. Try to do some practice tests in the <u>same format</u> as the test you'll be taking, so you know what to <u>expect</u> on the day.

What's in the 11+ Maths Test

Get your brain ready for Maths by reading about the different topics in the test.

Maths *involves* **Solving Number Problems**

1) You should have covered <u>most</u> of the Maths topics that will be on the test <u>at school</u>. However, you <u>may not</u> have learnt about all of them — for example, <u>algebra</u>.

2) We've grouped the topics that usually come up into <u>seven sections</u> in this book.

Number Knowledge

You'll need to be able to recognise <u>different types</u> of numbers. You'll need to look for <u>number patterns</u> and use <u>place value</u> and <u>rounding</u> to solve number problems.

You might not be tested on questions from every topic in the real test.

Working with Numbers

You'll need to use <u>addition</u>, <u>subtraction</u>, <u>multiplication</u> or <u>division</u> to answer these questions. You might also be asked to use or solve <u>algebraic expressions</u>.

Number Problems

You may be given <u>mixed calculations</u> where you have to use <u>more than one</u> operation (e.g. multiplication and addition). Or you could be given <u>word problems</u> where you need to use information in the question to find the answer.

Data Handling

Some questions use <u>data</u> in <u>tables</u> and <u>graphs</u>. You'll need to be able to find information in a table and know how to read different types of graphs.

Shape and Space

You may be tested on the names and properties of <u>2D</u> and <u>3D shapes</u>. Other questions may ask about <u>symmetry</u>, <u>coordinates</u>, <u>volume</u>, <u>area</u> and <u>perimeter</u>. You might also have to imagine shapes being rotated to solve <u>shape problems</u>.

Units and Measures

You may be tested on <u>units</u> and <u>time</u>. You'll need to be able to choose the correct unit for a <u>measurement</u> and to <u>convert</u> between different units (e.g. mm and cm).

Mixed Problems

There might also be questions that cover <u>more than one</u> topic. For example, you may be given a question where you have to read a graph and do some calculations.

How to Prepare for the 11+

Give yourself a head start with your Maths preparation — be organised and plan ahead.

Divide your Preparation into Stages

1) You should find a way to prepare for the 11+ that suits you. This may depend on how much time you have before the test. Here's a good way to plan your Maths practice:

> Do the Benchmark Test at the front of this book. Ask an adult to mark it for you.
>
> ⬇
>
> Learn strategies for answering different question types using this Study Book.
>
> ⬇
>
> Do plenty of practice questions, concentrating on the question types you find tricky.
>
> ⬇
>
> Sit some practice papers to prepare you for the real test.

2) When you first start answering 11+ Maths questions, try to solve the questions without making any mistakes, rather than working quickly.

3) Once you feel confident about the questions, then you can build up your speed.

4) You can do this by asking an adult to time you as you answer a set of questions, or by seeing how many questions you can answer in a certain amount of time, e.g. 5 minutes. You can then try to beat your time or score.

5) As you get closer to the test day, work on getting a balance between speed and accuracy — that's what you're aiming for when you sit the real test.

There are Many Ways to Practise the Skills you Need

The best way to tackle 11+ Maths is to do lots of practice. This isn't the only thing that will help though — there are other ways you can build up the skills you need for the test:

1) Practise your times tables with a friend by taking it in turns to test each other.

2) Divide up a cake, a pizza or a pie between a certain number of people. Work out what fraction each person is given.

3) Try drawing different shapes on a piece of paper. Use a small mirror to find lines of symmetry and work out what the shapes look like when they've been reflected.

4) Play games that involve counting like darts or MONOPOLY® to help you practise number calculations. You could also do activities like sudoku to help you to develop your problem solving skills and play Battleships to practise using coordinates.

Place Value

Place value is about knowing the value of all the digits in a number.

Warm-Up Activity

Let's start with a quick warm-up.
Which of the following numbers is the biggest and which is the smallest?

10   10 000   100   1   1000

The *Value* of a *Digit* depends on its *Place* in a *Number*

Each Digit in a Whole Number has a different Value

1) This example shows what each of the digits are worth in a 7-digit number — **1 256 297**.

Millions	Hundreds of thousands	Tens of thousands	Thousands	Hundreds	Tens	Units
↓	↓	↓	↓	↓	↓	↓
1	**2**	**5**	**6**	**2**	**9**	**7**
1 million, or 1 000 000.	2 hundred thousand, or 200 000.	5 tens of thousands, or 50 000.	6 thousand, or 6 000.	2 hundred, or 200.	9 tens, or 90.	7 units, or 7.

2) Each digit has the same value as 10 lots of the digit to its right, e.g. 1 hundred is equal to 10 tens.

3) Whole numbers have a greater value when there are more digits, e.g. 1 256 297 has a greater value than 256 297 because it has a millions digit.

4) When comparing whole numbers that have the same number of digits, you need to look at the value of each digit. For example, 254 is greater than 249. They have the same number in the hundreds column, but 254 has a greater number in the tens column than 249.

Each Digit in a Decimal Number has a different Value

1) This example shows you what each of the digits are worth in a decimal number — **1.365**.

Units	Decimal Point	Tenths	Hundredths	Thousandths
↓	↓	↓	↓	↓
1	**.**	**3**	**6**	**5**
1 unit, or 1		3 tenths, or 0.3	6 hundredths, or 0.06	5 thousandths, or 0.005

2) Each digit has the same value as 10 lots of the digit to its right, e.g. 1 tenth is equal to 10 hundredths.

3) When comparing decimal numbers you need to look at each digit in turn. For example, 0.56 is greater than 0.53. They have the same number in the tenths column, but 0.56 has a greater number in the hundredths column than 0.53.

11+ *Style* Questions

> **Q** What number is the arrow pointing to on this number line?
>
>
>
> 7.0   7.1

Method

1) Look at the <u>numbers</u> which are given and <u>how many points</u> there are on the number line.

    The answer is between 7.0 and 7.1, and there are ten points on the number line.
    The difference between 7.0 and 7.1 is one tenth, or 0.1. 0.1 is made up of ten hundredths,
    so each of the ten points on the number line is equal to one hundredth, or 0.01.

2) Count along the points to <u>where</u> the <u>arrow</u> is located on the number line.

    The arrow is pointing to the 6th point to the right of 7.0 on the number line, which means that this
    point is equal to 6 hundredths or 0.06. So the value of this point is 7 units and 6 hundredths, or 7.06.

> **Q** Luca, Steve, Flo, Sue and Tom all drove one lap around a Go-Kart track. They put their results in a table.
>
> Who drove the quickest?
>
> | Name | Time (seconds) |
> | --- | --- |
> | Luca | 49.7 |
> | Steve | 49.65 |
> | Flo | 49.92 |
> | Sue | 49.84 |
> | Tom | 50.1 |

Method

1) To find out who drove the <u>quickest</u> you need to find the <u>shortest time</u>, which means that you're looking for the <u>lowest value number</u>.

    Look at the tens and the units of each driver's time. Tom's time is the
    slowest because 50 (which has 5 tens) is greater than 49 (which has 4 tens).

2) <u>Luca</u>, <u>Steve</u>, <u>Flo</u> and <u>Sue</u> all have the <u>same number</u> of <u>tens</u> and <u>units</u> in their time, <u>49</u>. So you then need to look at the <u>first decimal number</u> of their times.

    They each have a different value for the first decimal place. Steve has
    a lower number of tenths than the others, 6, so his time is quickest.

Practice Questions

1) Which of these is the smallest number?

    A 8.47   **B** 8.543   **C** 8.465   **D** 8.449   **E** 8.43

2) Which of these pairs of numbers are equally distant from 7?

    A 6.97 and 7.3   **B** 6.89 and 7.11   **C** 6.8 and 7.02   **D** 6.94 and 7.1   **E** 6.9 and 7.19

Rounding Up and Down

You guessed it — you can round numbers up or down to give an estimated value.

The **Number 5** is **Important** when you're **Rounding Numbers**

1) To round any number you need to follow a <u>simple rule</u>:

  - If the digit to the right of the one you're rounding is less than 5 then you round down.
  - If the digit to the right of the one you're rounding is 5 or more then you round up.

For example, to round <u>17 872</u> to the <u>nearest 100</u>, you need to round the digit in the <u>hundreds column</u>.

> **17 872** — The digit in the hundreds column is 8.

Now look at the digit to its <u>right</u>, in the <u>tens column</u>, to see whether you need to <u>round up</u> or <u>down</u>.

> **17 872** — The digit in the tens column is 7, so you round up 17 872 to 17 900.

2) You can use this method for rounding <u>decimals</u> too. For example, to round <u>1.428</u> to <u>one decimal place</u> (or the <u>nearest tenth</u>), you need to round the digit in the <u>tenths column</u>.

Rounding to two decimal places means rounding to the nearest hundredth. Three decimal places means to the nearest thousandth.

> **1.428** — The digit in the tenths column is 4.

3) To work out whether to <u>round</u> this digit <u>up</u> or <u>down</u> you need to look at the digit to its <u>right</u> — in the <u>hundredths column</u>.

> **1.428** — The digit in the hundredths column is 2, so you round down 1.428 to 1.4.

11+ Style Questions

 Q What is 46.98 rounded to one decimal place?

Method

1) Work out which <u>digit</u> you need to <u>round</u>.

   One decimal place is the first digit after the decimal point — 46.98.

2) Look at the <u>digit</u> to the <u>right</u> of the digit you need to round and work out whether you need to <u>round up</u> or <u>round down</u>.

   The digit to the right of the digit you need to round is 8 — 46.98.
   8 is more than 5 so you need to round up. Rounding up 9 tenths will give you 10 tenths, which is equal to 1 unit. This will increase the digit in the units column from 6 to 7 and leave 0 tenths. So 46.98 rounded to one decimal place is 47.0, or 47.

> **Q** Which of these is 1500?
>
>   A 1508 to the nearest 10   D 1498 to the nearest 10
>   B 1448 to the nearest 100   E 1504 to the nearest 1000
>   C 1562 to the nearest 100

Method

1) Look at <u>each option</u> one by one.

   A   1508: 0 is being rounded, 8 is more than 5 — 1508 rounds up to 1510 not 1500.
   B   1448: 4 is being rounded, 4 is less than 5 — 1448 rounds down to 1400 not 1500.
   C   1562: 5 is being rounded, 6 is more than 5 — 1562 rounds up to 1600 not 1500.
   D   1498: 9 is being rounded, 8 is more than 5 — 1498 rounds up to 1500.
   So the answer is D.

2) If you have time you can <u>check</u> your answer by looking at the <u>last option</u>.

   E   1504: 1 is being rounded, 5 is 5 or more — 1504 rounds up to 2000 not 1500.

> **Q** Round 43.389 kg to the nearest 10 grams.
>   A 50 kg   D 40 kg
>   B 43.4 kg   E 43.39 kg
>   C 43 kg

Method

1) You need to find <u>43.389 kg</u> to the <u>nearest 10 grams</u> —
   it'll be <u>easier</u> to round this figure if you <u>convert</u> it into <u>grams</u>.

   A kilogram is the same as 1000 grams, so multiply 43.389 by 1000. 43.389 kg is 43 389 g.

2) Work out which digit is in the <u>tens</u> column and look at the digit to its
   <u>right</u> (in the <u>units</u> column) to see whether you need to <u>round up</u> or <u>down</u>.

   43 389: 8 is being rounded, 9 is more than 5 so 43 389 rounds up to 43 390.
   To convert this back into kilograms you just need to divide 43 390 by 1000.
   The answer is 43.39 kg.

Tips and Tricks for Multiple Choice

You can sometimes estimate the answer to tricky addition and subtraction questions by using rounding. If you had to work out 4988 + 507 you could round both numbers to 5000 and 500 to estimate the answer. 5000 + 500 = 5500. So the answer to 4988 + 507 is roughly 5500.

Practice Question

1) Round 174 782 to the nearest ten thousand.

   A 174 800   **B** 180 000   **C** 170 800   **D** 170 000   **E** 175 000

Section One — Number Knowledge

Number Knowledge

It's really useful to know a few facts about different types of numbers.

Warm-Up Activity

1) Borrow a <u>thermometer</u>. Put the thermometer in a <u>cold place</u>, such as a <u>freezer</u>. After <u>five minutes</u> write down the <u>temperature</u> it shows.

2) Then put the thermometer in a <u>warm place</u>, such as near a <u>radiator</u>. After <u>five minutes</u> write down the <u>temperature</u> it shows.

3) See if you can work out the <u>difference</u> in <u>temperature</u> between the <u>two places</u>.

Negative Numbers are *Numbers Below 0*

1) You can use <u>number lines</u> to work out the <u>value</u> of <u>negative numbers</u>.

2) The numbers on the number line <u>increase</u> from <u>left to right</u>. So <u>-1</u> is <u>greater than -6</u>.

3) <u>Number lines</u> can be used to help you with calculations that involve <u>negative numbers</u>. For example to work out 2 − 9, just count back 9 places from 2 along the number line:

You can use *Symbols* to show whether one number is *Bigger* or *Smaller* than *Another*

There are <u>two symbols</u> you can use:

< means 'is less than'. For example, -3 is less than 2 or **-3 < 2**.
> means 'is greater than'. For example, 7 is greater than 5 or **7 > 5**.

Whole Numbers are either *Odd* or *Even*

1) An <u>even number</u> is any whole number that can be <u>exactly divided</u> by <u>two</u> to give another <u>whole number</u>. For example, <u>6</u> is an <u>even number</u> because 6 ÷ 2 = 3.

2) An <u>odd number</u> is any whole number that can't be <u>divided</u> by <u>two</u> to give another <u>whole number</u>. For example, <u>5</u> is an <u>odd number</u> because 5 ÷ 2 = 2.5.

Even numbers end in 0, 2, 4, 6 or 8. Odd numbers end in 1, 3, 5, 7 or 9.

Factors of a number are **Whole Numbers** that divide **Exactly** into it

1) The factors of a number are all the whole numbers that divide that number exactly (so there's no remainder). For example the factors of 9 are 1, 3 and 9: 9 ÷ 1 = 9, 9 ÷ 3 = 3 and 9 ÷ 9 = 1.

2) If a question asks for the common factors of some numbers, you need to find the factors that the numbers all share.

3) Here's how to find the common factors of 12, 24 and 36.

> Find the factors of each number, then work out which factors are the same for all three numbers.
>
> > The factors of 12 are: 1, 2, 3, 4, 6 and 12.
> > The factors of 24 are: 1, 2, 3, 4, 6, 8, 12 and 24.
> > The factors of 36 are: 1, 2, 3, 4, 6, 9, 12, 18 and 36.
> > 1, 2, 3, 4, 6 and 12 are all common factors of 12, 24 and 36.

A **Multiple** is the **Result** of **Multiplying** one **Whole Number** by another

1) The multiples of a number are just the times table for that number, e.g. multiples of 4 are 4, 8, 12, 16 etc.

2) If a question asks for a common multiple of some numbers, you need to find a multiple that the numbers all share.

3) Here's how to find a common multiple of 3, 4 and 6.

> Find the first few multiples of each number and check if any of them are the same. If not, work out a few more multiples, then try again.
>
> > The first six multiples of 3 are: 3, 6, 9, 12, 15 and 18.
> > The first six multiples of 4 are: 4, 8, 12, 16, 20 and 24.
> > The first six multiples of 6 are: 6, 12, 18, 24, 30, 36.
> > 12 is a common multiple of 3, 4 and 6.

Prime Numbers only have **Two Factors**

1) A prime number is a number with exactly two factors — the number itself and one. For example, 23 is a prime number — the only factors of 23 are 1 and 23.

2) 1 is NOT a prime number — it doesn't have exactly two factors.

3) Apart from 2 and 5, all prime numbers end in 1, 3, 7 or 9 (but not all numbers ending in 1, 3, 7 or 9 are prime numbers).

4) The only even prime number is 2.

> The first ten prime numbers are: 2, 3, 5, 7, 11, 13, 17, 19, 23 and 29.

A *Whole Number Multiplied* by *Itself* gives a *Square Number*

1) For example, if you multiply 4 by itself (4 × 4) you get 16 — a square number.

2) The first 12 square numbers are:

1	4	9	16	25	36	49	64	81	100	121	144
(1 × 1)	(2 × 2)	(3 × 3)	(4 × 4)	(5 × 5)	(6 × 6)	(7 × 7)	(8 × 8)	(9 × 9)	(10 × 10)	(11 × 11)	(12 × 12)

3) You can show a number is squared using a small 2, e.g. five squared (5 × 5) can be written as "5^2".

11+ *Style* Questions

> **Q** The sum of the first three square numbers is 14.
> What is the sum of the first 6 square numbers?

Method

1) You're told that the first three square numbers add up to 14. You need to work out the sum of the 4th, 5th and 6th square numbers and add it to 14. The 4th, 5th and 6th square numbers are:

4^2 4 × 4 = 16
5^2 5 × 5 = 25
6^2 6 × 6 = 36

2) Now add together 14, 16, 25 and 36 to get the answer.

14 + 16 + 25 + 36 = 91.

> **Q** Emily has bought some sweets. She gives them all away to her friends. Each friend got an equal number of sweets and they were all given more than one sweet. How many sweets could she have bought?
>
> 19   23   24   29   31

The question doesn't say how many friends Emily has — but she has more than one because it says she has "friends" and not "a friend".

Method

1) You might recognise that all of the amounts, except 24, are prime numbers (prime numbers have no factors other than one and the number itself).

   If the number of sweets is a prime number, e.g. 23, then they can only be equally distributed between one friend or a group of 23 friends. The question shows that there is more than one friend and they all get more than one sweet. So none of these are right.

2) The answer to the question is 24 because that is the only number that has any factors other than 1 and itself. For example, if Emily had 24 sweets she could give 8 friends 3 sweets each, or 4 friends could have 6 sweets each, etc.

3) If you're not sure if a number is prime then you can try to find the number's factors.

   For example, you could work out if 19 has any factors other than 1 or 19. Divide 19 by possible factors to see if you get a whole number. This will take time so it'd be useful to memorise some prime numbers.

Q Two of the numbers are missing from this sorting diagram.

	Multiple of 3	Not a Multiple of 3
Square	36 144 ?	4 64 16
Not Square	?	2

Which of the following could be the missing numbers?

A 6 and 3 D 81 and 3

B 3 and 25 E 81 and 19

C 81 and 9

Method

1) <u>Both</u> of the missing numbers are <u>multiples of 3</u>, one is a <u>square number</u> and <u>one isn't</u>.
   Start off by finding which of the answer options have <u>two multiples of 3</u>.

   3, 6, 9 and 81 are all multiples of 3, 19 and 25 are not — options A, C and D all have two multiples of 3.

2) Now work out which one of these options has <u>only one square number</u>.

   A   6 and 3 are not square numbers.
   C   81 and 9 are both square numbers ($3 \times 3 = 9$, $9 \times 9 = 81$).
   D   81 is a square number, but 3 is not — D is the answer.

Q Which of these numbers will go into the shaded section of the Venn diagram?

A 4 D 13

B 7 E 27

C 9

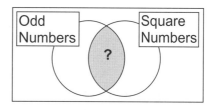

Method

1) Data that's put into a <u>Venn diagram</u> must <u>match</u> its <u>labels</u>.
   <u>Odd numbers</u> must go in the <u>left-hand circle</u> of this Venn diagram, and
   <u>square numbers</u> can only go in the <u>right-hand circle</u>. Where the Venn diagram <u>overlaps</u>
   the data must match <u>both labels</u> — so numbers in this section must be <u>odd and square</u>.
   Data that <u>doesn't match</u> any of the labels must go in the <u>box outside the circles</u>.

2) Numbers that are both odd and square must go in the shaded section.
   Start off by working out which of the options are <u>square numbers</u>.

   4 and 9 are both square numbers: $4 = 2 \times 2$, $9 = 3 \times 3$.

3) Then, work out which of <u>4</u> and <u>9</u> is an <u>odd number</u>.

   4 is even because it's divisible by 2. 9 is odd because it isn't divisible by 2 — C is the answer.

Practice Questions

1) Which of these statements is true?

   A All factors of 24 are multiples of 2.   **D** A prime number can also be a square number.
   B 13 and 52 have no common factors.   **E** A prime number can be a multiple of 3.
   C All numbers ending in a 3 are multiples of 3.

2) Which of these numbers is not a factor of 72?

   A 4 **B** 6 **C** 7 **D** 8 **E** 9

Section One — Number Knowledge

Number Sequences

You need to follow the rule of a sequence to get from one number to the next.

Warm-Up Activity

What is the <u>difference</u> between <u>each number</u> in the sequence below?
See if you can work out what the <u>next number</u> in the sequence will be.

2   11   20   29   38

Some **Number Sequences** follow a **Pattern** you **Already Know**

1) You might <u>spot</u> a <u>pattern</u> in a <u>number sequence</u> because you recognise the numbers.

> 2, 3, 5, 7... — are all prime numbers going up in order.
> 25, 20, 15, 10... — are all multiples of 5 going down in order.
> 1, 4, 9, 16... — are all square numbers going up in order.

2) Once you know the <u>pattern</u> you can work out what the <u>next number</u> in the sequence will be.

> 1, 3, 5, 7... are all odd numbers going up in order. So the next number in the sequence will be 9.

3) You can also work out later numbers in the sequence. For example, to find the seventh number in this sequence of <u>odd numbers</u>, follow the <u>same pattern</u> until the seventh number.

> 1, 3, 5, 7, 9, 11, 13 — the seventh number in this sequence is 13.

You might need to **Find** the **Rule** for a **Number Sequence**

1) You might be given a <u>more difficult</u> number sequence, e.g. 4, 5, 7, 10, 14.

2) You'll need to work out the <u>rule</u> that the <u>number sequence</u> follows. One way to do this is to look at the <u>difference</u> between <u>each number</u> in the sequence.

> 4   5   7   10   14
> + 1 + 2 + 3 + 4
>
> The amount you need to add to get the next number in the sequence goes up by 1 each time. The next number in the sequence will be 14 + 5 = 19.

3) Make sure you look at <u>all</u> the values in the sequence when you're working out the rule. For example, the <u>start</u> of this sequence looks like it follows the <u>same</u> <u>rule</u> as the one above — but if you look at <u>all</u> the values, you can see the rule is actually to <u>add</u> together the <u>previous two numbers</u> in the sequence:

> 2, 3, 5, 8, 13   ⟹   2 + 3 = 5, 3 + 5 = 8, 5 + 8 = 13.

11+ *Style* Questions

Q Scott started from the number 14 and counted back in steps of 6.
Which of these numbers did he count?

    A 4   B 1   C 0   D -2   E -4

Method

1) Write out the <u>number sequence</u> for this question and see which number is included in it. Writing out the sequence will help you <u>avoid</u> any <u>mistakes</u>.

    Make sure you apply the correct rule — subtract 6 each time.

2) Out of the options you're given, <u>only -4</u> appears in the <u>sequence</u>. So the answer is <u>E</u>.

Q There are 9 small triangles in this shape. The shape is three triangles high. How many small triangles would there be in a shape that's five triangles high?

Method

1) You need to <u>find</u> what the <u>sequence</u> is.

    If the shape is one triangle high it has 1 triangle.
    If the shape is two triangles high it has 4 triangles.
    If the shape is three triangles high it has 9 triangles.

2) So the <u>sequence</u> for the <u>number</u> of <u>triangles</u> is <u>1</u>, <u>4</u>, <u>9</u>. To find the <u>5th number</u> in this <u>sequence</u> you need to work out if there's a <u>pattern</u>.

3) The <u>difference</u> between each number in the sequence <u>increases by 2</u> each time — each row added has <u>two more small triangles</u> than the last one. Now work out what the <u>5th number</u> in the <u>sequence</u> will be.

    The difference increases by two each time, so apply this rule until you reach the 5th number.

4) If the shape was <u>five triangles high</u> it would have <u>25 small triangles</u> in it.

Practice Question

1) Jake is building a wall. He lays four bricks in the first hour, 5 in the second and 6 in the third. Each hour he continues to add one more brick than he laid in the previous hour. How many bricks will he have laid after 6 hours?

      1 hour   2 hours   3 hours

Section One — Number Knowledge

Fractions

Fractions are a bit tricky, but you'll be fine once you've learnt the basics.

Fractions are *Parts* of a *Whole Number*

1) A <u>fraction</u> looks like this:

The bottom number of a fraction is the denominator. It tells you how many equal parts something is split into.

$\frac{4}{9}$

The top number of a fraction is the numerator. It tells you how many equal parts you've got.

2) Fractions can be shown using <u>shapes</u>.

This triangle is split into 9 equal parts. 4 out of the 9 parts are shaded. So the fraction of the triangle that's shaded is $\frac{4}{9}$.

3) To find a <u>fraction</u> of a <u>number</u> (e.g. three fifths of 15), <u>divide</u> the <u>number</u> by the <u>fraction's denominator</u>. Then <u>multiply</u> the result by the <u>fraction's numerator</u>.

$\frac{3}{5}$ of 15. $15 \div 5 = 3$. Then, $3 \times 3 = 9$ ◄━━ So $\frac{3}{5}$ of 15 is 9.

Divide by the denominator   Multiply by the numerator

4) You can see this more clearly with a <u>diagram</u>:

To find $\frac{3}{5}$ of 15 apples you need to divide 15 by 5. That gives you 5 groups of 3 apples. So $\frac{3}{5}$ = 3 groups of 3 apples, or 9 apples.

Some *Fractions* are *Bigger Than 1*

1) You can write <u>fractions</u> that are <u>bigger than 1</u> as <u>improper fractions</u> or <u>mixed numbers</u>.

2) <u>Improper fractions</u> have a numerator that's <u>bigger</u> than the denominator. For example:

$13\frac{}{8}$ → written as $\frac{13}{8}$

1 whole is the same as 8 eighths (or $\frac{8}{8}$) so this fraction is greater than 1. 13 eighths is the same as one whole plus another $\frac{5}{8}$.

3) <u>Mixed numbers</u> have <u>both</u> a whole number and a fraction. For example:

$1\frac{5}{8}$

This fraction is greater than 1 — there is 1 whole plus another $\frac{5}{8}$.

Equivalent Fractions are Fractions which are Equal

1) For example, ¼ and ⅖ are <u>equivalent fractions</u> because they're <u>equal</u>. You can show this using <u>shapes</u>:

2) To find an <u>equivalent fraction</u>, <u>multiply</u> the <u>numerator</u> and the <u>denominator</u> by the <u>same number</u>. So ⅖ is <u>equivalent</u> to ⁴⁄₁₀ , ⁶⁄₁₅ and ⁸⁄₂₀.

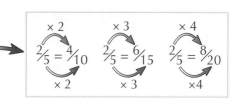

3) You can also find <u>equivalent fractions</u> by <u>dividing</u> both the <u>numerator</u> and the <u>denominator</u> by the <u>same number</u>. This is called <u>simplifying</u> a <u>fraction</u>. For example ⁵⁵⁄₁₀₀ is equivalent to ¹¹⁄₂₀ .

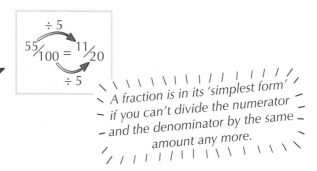

A fraction is in its 'simplest form' if you can't divide the numerator and the denominator by the same amount any more.

You can Add and Subtract Fractions

1) <u>Adding</u> and <u>subtracting</u> fractions is easy if they <u>both</u> have the <u>same denominator</u>. All you need to do is <u>add</u> or <u>subtract</u> the <u>numerators</u> and keep the <u>denominator</u> the <u>same</u>.

$$\tfrac{2}{5} + \tfrac{2}{5} = \tfrac{4}{5} \qquad \tfrac{4}{5} - \tfrac{1}{5} = \tfrac{3}{5}$$

2) To <u>add</u> or <u>subtract</u> fractions which have <u>different denominators</u>, change them so they have the <u>same denominator</u>. You can do this by making them into <u>equivalent fractions</u>.

⅖ + ³⁄₁₀ — to add these fractions you need to change them so they have the same denominator. One way to do this is to make ⅖ a fraction with 10 as its denominator.

Both fractions now have the same denominator, so you can add them together.

11+ *Style* Questions

Q How many ninths are there in 5?

    A 5   B 9   C 25   D 45   E 50

Method

1) Work out how many <u>ninths</u> there are in <u>1</u>.

    There are 9 ninths in 1 ($\frac{9}{9} = 1$).

2) So, in <u>5</u> there will be <u>5 sets</u> of <u>9 ninths</u>, or <u>5 × 9</u>.

    $5 \times 9 = 45$. There are 45 ninths in 5.

Q A coat is originally priced at £32.
Its price is reduced to $\frac{3}{4}$ of the original price.
What is the price of the coat now?

Method

1) You need to find $\frac{3}{4}$ of <u>£32</u>. First, <u>divide 32</u> by the <u>denominator</u> of the <u>fraction</u>.

    4 is the denominator in $\frac{3}{4}$. So, $32 \div 4 = 8$.
    This means that $\frac{1}{4}$ of £32 = £8.

2) Now <u>multiply 8</u> by the <u>numerator</u>.

    If $\frac{1}{4} = 8$, then $\frac{3}{4}$ is $3 \times 8 = 24$.

3) The coat costs <u>£24</u>.

4) You could also use this method in a <u>different way</u>. Start by <u>multiplying</u> the <u>number</u> by the <u>numerator</u> and then <u>divide</u> the <u>result</u> by the <u>denominator</u>.

    3 is the numerator in $\frac{3}{4}$. So, $32 \times 3 = 96$.
    Then divide 96 by the denominator, which is 4.
    $96 \div 4 = 24$. The coat costs £24.

Practice Questions

1) Lydia and Rose each have a pie. Their pies are exactly the same size.
Lydia gave two fifths of her pie to Gemma.
Rose gave Gemma one fifth of her pie.
Which statement is correct?

    A Gemma has more pie than Lydia.   **D** Gemma has the same amount of pie as Rose.
    B Gemma has more pie than Rose.   **E** Gemma has the same amount of pie as Lydia.
    C Rose and Lydia together have exactly twice as much pie as Gemma.

2) Ilya and Alex share two bags of apples. Each bag contains 6 apples.
Ilya took $\frac{1}{4}$ of the apples. Alex took $\frac{2}{3}$ of the apples.
How many apples were left?

    A 0   **B** 1   **C** 2   **D** 3   **E** 4

Percentages, Fractions and Decimals

You can write an amount of something as a decimal, a fraction or a percentage. This page will show you how percentages, fractions and decimals are related, and how to convert between them.

Warm-Up Activity

1) Look at the back of some <u>tins of food</u>, <u>cereal boxes</u> or <u>sauce bottles</u> and see if you can find <u>five</u> different <u>percentages</u> (they'll look like this '**23%**').

2) Once you've worked through this page, see if you can <u>convert</u> the <u>percentages</u> into <u>fractions</u> and <u>decimals</u>.

You can **Convert** between **Percentages**, **Fractions** and **Decimals**

Decimals can be Converted into Percentages

1) To convert a <u>decimal</u> into a <u>percentage</u> you need to <u>multiply</u> the <u>decimal</u> by <u>100</u>, e.g. $0.53 \times 100 = \underline{53\%}$.

2) You can also convert <u>percentages</u> into <u>decimals</u> — you just <u>divide</u> the <u>percentage</u> by <u>100</u>, e.g. $72\% = 72 \div 100 = \underline{0.72}$.

Per cent can also be written as % — it just means "out of 100". 17 per cent, which is 17 out of 100, can also be written as 17%.

Fractions can be Converted into Percentages

1) Converting fractions with <u>100</u> as the <u>denominator</u> into <u>percentages</u> is <u>easy</u>. <u>Hundredths</u> are already "<u>out of 100</u>". So the <u>numerator</u> will be the <u>percentage</u>, e.g. $^{23}/_{100} = \underline{23\%}$.

2) Other fractions can be <u>converted</u> into <u>percentages</u> too. You just need to make an <u>equivalent fraction</u> (see p. 15) with <u>100</u> as the <u>denominator</u>.

$^{7}/_{20} = {}^{35}/_{100} = 35\%$
×5 ... ×5

3) You can write <u>any percentage</u> as a <u>fraction</u>. You put the <u>percentage</u> on the <u>top</u> of the <u>fraction</u> (the <u>numerator</u>) and <u>100</u> on the <u>bottom</u> (the <u>denominator</u>), e.g. $\underline{17\%} = {}^{17}/_{100}$.

Fractions can also be Converted into Decimals

1) To <u>convert</u> a <u>fraction</u> into a <u>decimal</u> you first need to make it into an <u>equivalent fraction</u> with <u>100</u> as its <u>denominator</u>.

2) Then <u>divide</u> the <u>numerator</u> of the <u>equivalent fraction</u> by <u>100</u> to get the <u>decimal</u>.

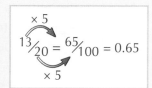

$^{13}/_{20} = {}^{65}/_{100} = 0.65$
×5 ... ×5

3) To convert a <u>decimal</u> into a <u>fraction</u> you just do the <u>reverse</u>. <u>Multiply</u> the decimal by <u>100</u>, then put this as the <u>numerator</u> above a <u>denominator of 100</u>. E.g. $\underline{0.29} = {}^{29}/_{100}$.

These are very common fractions as percentages and decimals — make sure you know them:
$\frac{1}{4} = 25\%$ or 0.25 $\frac{3}{4} = 75\%$ or 0.75 $\frac{1}{2} = 50\%$ or 0.5 $\frac{1}{10} = 10\%$ or 0.1 $\frac{1}{5} = 20\%$ or 0.2

11+ *Style* Questions

 Q Find the correct statement.

A $7\frac{1}{4} < 7.2$ D $7\frac{1}{5} = 7.2$

B $7\frac{1}{5} > 7.2$ E $7\frac{1}{2} < 7.2$

C $7\frac{1}{10} > 7.2$

Method

1) <u>Convert</u> each of the <u>fractions</u> into a <u>decimal</u> so you can <u>compare</u> the <u>numbers</u>.

$$7\frac{1}{4} = 7\frac{25}{100} = 7.25$$
$$7\frac{1}{5} = 7\frac{20}{100} = 7.2$$
$$7\frac{1}{10} = 7\frac{10}{100} = 7.1$$
$$7\frac{1}{2} = 7\frac{50}{100} = 7.5$$

2) Now you can check <u>each statement</u>.
Remember, '<' means <u>less than</u> and '>' means <u>greater than</u>.

A 7.25 < 7.2. Incorrect.

B 7.2 > 7.2. Incorrect.

C 7.1 > 7.2. Incorrect.

D 7.2 = 7.2. Correct. So D is the answer.

E 7.5 < 7.2. Incorrect.

Q A bottle of tomato sauce contains 10% sugar.
What fraction of the tomato sauce is sugar?

A $\frac{2}{5}$ B $\frac{1}{10}$ C $\frac{1}{4}$ D $\frac{1}{2}$ E $\frac{1}{20}$

Method

1) You might recognise that <u>10%</u> = $\frac{1}{10}$. If you don't then you'll need to <u>work it out</u>.

Convert 10% into a fraction. 10% = $\frac{10}{100}$.

2) <u>None</u> of the options is $\frac{10}{100}$, which means that one of them must be <u>equivalent</u> to it. <u>All</u> of the options are fractions in their <u>simplest form</u>, so you need to <u>simplify</u> $\frac{10}{100}$ to find the answer.

If some of the options aren't in their simplest form, simplify them first.

The numerator and the denominator are both multiples of 10 — divide them both by 10 to find the simplest form of the fraction.

$$\frac{10}{100} = \frac{1}{10}$$

3) <u>Compare</u> your simplified fraction with the <u>answer options</u> — the answer is <u>B</u>.

Q Which one of these is the greatest?

   A ⅕ of 45   B 25% of 40   C ⅓ of 30   D 80% of 20   E ¾ of 20

Method

1) Work out the value of <u>each option</u> which involves a <u>fraction</u>. To work out the <u>fraction</u> of a <u>number</u> you need to <u>divide</u> the <u>number</u> by the <u>denominator</u> and <u>multiply</u> it by the <u>numerator</u>.

   > A: ⅕ of 45. 45 ÷ 5 = 9. 9 × 1 = 9.
   >
   > C: ⅓ of 30. 30 ÷ 3 = 10. 10 × 1 = 10.
   >
   > E: ¾ of 20. 20 ÷ 4 = 5. 5 × 3 = 15.

2) Work out the value of <u>each option</u> which involves a <u>percentage</u>. To work out the <u>percentage</u> of a number you could <u>convert</u> the <u>percentage</u> to a <u>fraction</u>. Then follow the method for working out the <u>fraction</u> of a <u>number</u>.

   > B: 25% of 40 is the same as ¼ of 40. 40 ÷ 4 = 10. 10 × 1 = 10.
   >
   > D: 80% of 20 is the same as ⁸⁄₁₀ of 20. 20 ÷ 10 = 2. 2 × 8 = 16.

   Alternatively, to find a percentage of a number you can divide the number by 100 and multiply the result by the percentage you want to find.

3) The answer is <u>D</u> because <u>80%</u> of <u>20</u> is the <u>greatest number</u>.

Tips and Tricks for Percentages, Fractions and Decimals

Memorising some fractions as decimals and percentages will help you answer some questions much faster.

Practice Questions

1) What percentage of this triangle is shaded?

   A 10%   **B** 20%   **C** 25%   **D** 30%   **E** 40%

2) Marek asked all the children in year 5 what their favourite colour was. He made a chart to show his results.

   There are 90 children in year 5.

   How many children chose pink as their favourite colour?

   A 12   **B** 18   **C** 27   **D** 30   **E** 33

3) Which one of these is the smallest?

   A 25% of 4   **B** ¾ of 8   **C** ⅖ of 10   **D** 10% of 25   **E** ⅙ of 18

Addition

You've been adding numbers together for years. Here are a few of the question types you might get in the exam, and some methods you could use to answer them.

Warm-Up Activity

1) Ask someone else to join you and take it in turns to roll <u>three</u> dice.

2) <u>Add together</u> the three numbers. Give yourself 1 point if you score <u>8 or more</u>.

3) The first player to get <u>6 points</u> is the winner.

11+ Style Questions

> **Q** Marco has £4.13, Kyle has £3.42 and Janet has £8.70.
> How much money do they have in total?
>
> A   £15.95   D   £16.25
> B   £18.25   E   £14.25
> C   £17.85

Quick Method

1) You can <u>estimate</u> the answer to the question by <u>rounding</u> the numbers to the nearest pound to make <u>more manageable</u> numbers.

| £4.13 is rounded down to £4.00   £3.42 is rounded down to £3.00   £8.70 is rounded up to £9.00 |

2) Add the <u>rounded numbers together</u> to estimate the answer.

| £4.00 + £3.00 + £9.00 = £16.00 |

3) The answer is <u>around</u> £16.00. Looking at the options, the answer could be <u>A</u> or <u>D</u>.

4) As you rounded <u>down</u> by 55p (13p + 42p) and you rounded <u>up</u> by 30p, your estimate will be <u>lower</u> than the actual answer. So, the <u>actual answer</u> must be £16.25 — option <u>D</u>.

Written Method

1) An <u>alternative</u> method is to add the three values together in <u>columns</u>.

Add together the numbers in each column.

```
  4 . 1 3
  3 . 4 2
+ 8 . 7 0
─────────
1 6 . 2 5
      1
```

Remember to carry the digit over if the answer is more than 9.

Make sure that you line up the place value columns and the decimal points.

2) This method gives you the <u>exact answer</u>, £16.25.

Q The table shows the amount of juice in litres sold by Cathy on her market stall over 8 weeks.

Work out the total amount of juice Cathy sold from week 3 to week 6.

Week	Amount of juice sold (l)	Week	Amount of juice sold (l)
1	43.71	5	46.30
2	46.18	6	59.12
3	82.63	7	21.14
4	34.18	8	63.94

Method

1) This is a <u>standard answer</u> question — there are <u>no options</u> to choose from. So you need to find the <u>exact answer</u> — you <u>can't</u> use rounding.

2) The question is asking for the total sales from <u>week 3</u> to <u>week 6</u>, so find the <u>data</u> you need in the <u>table</u>.

> Week 3 = 82.63 litres   Week 5 = 46.30 litres
> Week 4 = 34.18 litres   Week 6 = 59.12 litres

3) Arrange the four weekly values into <u>columns</u>. <u>Add together</u> the numbers in each column.

Use the column method to find the exact answer.

$$
\begin{array}{r}
8\,2\,.\,6\,3 \\
3\,4\,.\,1\,8 \\
4\,6\,.\,3\,0 \\
+\,5\,9\,.\,1\,2 \\
\hline
2\,2\,2\,.\,2\,3 \\
2\;1\;\,1
\end{array}
$$

4) The total amount of juice sold from week 3 to week 6 by Cathy is <u>222.23 litres</u>.

Tips and Tricks for Addition Questions

When you've worked out an exact answer, you could check that your answer is sensible by using the rounding method to do a quick estimate.

Practice Questions

1) Katie buys a cycling helmet for £13.89, a bell for £3.35 and some gloves for £12.30. How much money does she spend?

   A £31.96   **B** £29.54   **C** £32.14   **D** £28.76   **E** £26.89

2) Rafid, Freia, Martin and John take part in a relay race. Rafid's leg took 12.37 seconds, Freia's leg took 11.88 seconds, Martin's leg took 13.24 seconds and John's leg took 10.94 seconds. What was their total time for the race?

Subtraction

Subtraction can get a bit tricky. All the more reason to get in lots of practice...

Warm-Up Activity

1) Choose <u>ten</u> numbers between <u>1 and 100</u>. Write them out on separate scraps of paper.

2) Lay the scraps of paper <u>face-down</u> on a table.

3) Turn over <u>two</u> scraps of paper and <u>subtract</u> the smaller number from the bigger number in your head. Use a calculator to <u>check</u> whether you got the answer right.

4) Turn the papers <u>back over</u> and <u>shuffle</u> them up a bit. Then pick <u>another two numbers</u>.

5) The game ends when you have <u>five correct answers</u>.

11+ Style Questions

> **Q** Emma has £13.10. She donates £2.21 to charity.
> How much money does Emma have left?
>
> | | | | |
> |---|---|---|---|
> | A | £10.89 | D | £11.79 |
> | B | £11.81 | E | £10.79 |
> | C | £9.89 | | |

Method 1

1) <u>Partition</u> the number that you are subtracting into its <u>units</u>, <u>tenths</u> and <u>hundredths</u>:

£2.21 splits up into £2 + £0.20 + £0.01

           units   tenths hundredths

2) <u>Subtract</u> each number <u>one at a time</u>:

£13.10 − £2.00 = £11.10
£11.10 − £0.20 = £10.90   ← Be careful here — you're changing the value in the units column as well as the tenths.
£10.90 − £0.01 = £10.89

Your answer is £10.89 — option A.

Method 2

1) You can also subtract numbers by writing them in <u>columns</u>.

2) Write the <u>number you're subtracting from first</u> and make sure the decimal points <u>line up</u>.

Subtract the numbers in each column.

$$1\,^2\cancel{3}\,.^1\cancel{0}\,\cancel{1}\,^10$$
$$-\quad 2\,.\,2\,1$$
$$\overline{1\,0\,.\,8\,9}$$

If you have to subtract a bigger number from a smaller number, make an exchange from the next place value column.

Q Five people ran two 200 m races.
Who had the greatest difference between
their time for race 1 and race 2?

Name	Race 1 (s)	Race 2 (s)
Jordan	22.48	23.95
Vanessa	23.07	24.76
Andrei	22.11	23.08
Rajpal	24.04	25.67
Stacey	23.45	24.40

A   Jordan   D   Rajpal
B   Vanessa   E   Stacey
C   Andrei

You could use a written method to work out the difference in time for each person, but it would take a lot of time.

Method

1) Start by underlining the difference between the times for each person.
   This will mean you don't have to work out the exact time for each person.

2) Estimate the difference by rounding each time to the nearest tenth.
   You need to subtract their fastest time from their slowest time.

> Jordan: Race 1 rounds to 22.50 and race 2 rounds to 24.00. 24.00 – 22.50 = 1.50 seconds.
> Vanessa: Race 1 rounds to 23.10 and race 2 rounds to 24.80. 24.80 – 23.10 = 1.70 seconds.
> Andrei: Race 1 rounds to 22.10 and race 2 rounds to 23.10. 23.10 – 22.10 = 1.00 seconds.
> Rajpal: Race 1 rounds to 24.00 and race 2 rounds to 25.70. 25.70 – 24.00 = 1.70 seconds.
> Stacey: Race 1 rounds to 23.50 and race 2 rounds to 24.40. 24.40 – 23.50 = 0.90 seconds.

Vanessa and Rajpal both have the greatest difference between their times, 1.70 seconds.

3) You can't tell just from rounding whether Vanessa or Rajpal have the greatest difference,
   so you need to work out the exact difference in their times. Use the partitioning method:

Vanessa
23.07 = 23.00 + 0.07
24.76 – 23.00 = 1.76
1.76 – 0.07 = 1.69

Rajpal
24.04 = 24.00 + 0.04
25.67 – 24.00 = 1.67
1.67 – 0.04 = 1.63

Remember to partition the smaller number.

4) The difference between Vanessa's times is greater than the difference between Rajpal's times.
   Your answer is B — Vanessa.

Practice Questions

1) Gavin's bath holds 75.63 litres of water when it is full. Gavin pours 48.28 litres of water
   into the bath. How many more litres of water would he need to fill the bath?
   A 27.45   **B** 27.75   **C** 26.95   **D** 28.15   **E** 27.35

2) The table shows the results of five students in
   two tests. Which student had the greatest
   increase in score between test 1 and test 2?

Name	Test 1 (%)	Test 2 (%)
Joe	57.6	61.5
Holly	60.2	63.8
Lucille	62.7	63.0
Dave	64.1	59.9
Anita	59.8	64.7

Multiplying and Dividing by 10, 100 and 1000

When you multiply or divide any number by 10, 100 or 1000, you just move the digits left or right.

Warm-Up Activity

Write down the following numbers in order from smallest to biggest.

6300

630

0.063

6.3

0.63

63

Move digits **Left** to **Multiply** by *10, 100* or *1000*

1) If you're multiplying a number by 10, move the digits one place to the left.

2.4 × 10 = 24

2) If you're multiplying a number by 100, move the digits two places to the left.

Add a zero here to fill in the gap before the decimal point.

75.9 × 100 = 7590

3) If you're multiplying a number by 1000, move the digits three places to the left.

This time you need to add two zeros before the decimal point.

27.1 × 1000 = 27 100

Move digits **Right** to **Divide** by *10, 100* or *1000*

1) If you're dividing a number by 10, move the digits one place to the right.

Add a zero before the decimal point to fill in the gap.

8.6 ÷ 10 = 0.86

2) If you're dividing a number by 100, move the digits two places to the right.

Add one zero before the decimal point and one zero after to fill in the gaps.

7.5 ÷ 100 = 0.075

3) If you're dividing a number by 1000, move the digits three places to the right.

Add a zero before the decimal point to fill in the gap.

600 ÷ 1000 = 0.600 = 0.6

11+ Style Questions

> **Q** Which of these calculations equals 843?
>
> | | | | |
> |---|---|---|---|
> | A | $84300 \div 10$ | D | 0.0843×1000 |
> | B | 0.843×1000 | E | 0.843×100 |
> | C | $84300 \div 1000$ | | |

Method

You can draw out the place value columns to help you if you're finding these calculations tricky.

1) Work out the answer to <u>each calculation</u>:

> | | |
> |---|---|
> | A | Move each digit one place to the right: $84300 \div 10 = 8430$ |
> | B | Move each digit three places to the left: $0.843 \times 1000 = 843$ |
> | C | Move each digit three places to the right: $84300 \div 1000 = 84.3$ |
> | D | Move each digit three places to the left: $0.0843 \times 1000 = 84.3$ |
> | E | Move each digit two places to the left: $0.843 \times 100 = 84.3$ |

2) The correct answer is 0.843×1000 — option <u>B</u>.

> **Q** $301 \times 10 = \ldots\ldots\ldots \div 100$
> Which number should fill in the blank?

Method

1) Multiply <u>301 by 10</u> to work out the <u>first part</u> of the calculation.

$$301 \times 10 = 3010$$ To multiply by ten, move each digit one place to the left.

2) The <u>second part</u> of the calculation must also <u>equal</u> 3010.

3) When you <u>divide</u> the missing number by <u>100</u>, it will equal <u>3010</u>.
So, calculate the missing number by doing the <u>inverse operation</u> — multiplying by 100.

$$3010 \times 100 = 301\,000$$ This time you multiply by 100, so each digit moves two places to the left.

4) That gives you the answer: <u>301 000</u>. You can check it's correct by dividing <u>301 000 by 100</u>. It should equal <u>3010</u>.

Practice Questions

1) Mark has sold 1000 tickets for a raffle. The tickets were sold in books of ten.
In total, Mark collected £375 for all 1000 tickets. How much did one book cost?
A £0.37   **B** £3.75   **C** £3.57   **D** £7.35   **E** £5.73

2) $4.2 \div 10 = \ldots\ldots\ldots \times 100$
What number should fill in the blank?

Section Two — Working with Numbers

Multiplication

There are a few types of multiplication question that you may be given
— these pages will show you how to tackle them.

Warm-Up Activity

1) Think of as many <u>different</u> multiplications as you can that will give the <u>numbers</u> on the cards.

2) See how many you can think of in <u>5 minutes</u>.

| 18 | 36 | 54 | 12 | 28 |

11+ Style Questions

> **Q** A DVD costs £3.99. How much will nine DVDs cost?
>
> A   £35.91   D   £35.97
> B   £36.00   E   £36.09
> C   £36.04

Quick Method

1) Round the cost of each DVD to the <u>nearest whole number</u>. Then multiply by <u>nine</u>.

> £3.99 rounds up to £4.00. £4.00 × 9 = £36.00

You added 1 penny for each DVD, and there were nine DVDs.

2) £36.00 is <u>not</u> the exact answer though. You added <u>nine pence</u> to this answer when you rounded the price of the DVDs. You need to <u>subtract nine pence</u> to reach the final answer.

> £36.00 – £0.09 = £35.91   Your answer is £35.91 — option A.

Written Method

1) You can multiply the numbers together in <u>columns</u>.

2) Make sure that you line up the <u>decimal point</u> and the <u>place value columns</u> in your answer.

```
        3 . 9 9      Multiply the hundredths,
    ×         9         tenths and units by 9.
    ─────────────
    3 5 . 9 1      Carry the left hand digit to the next
        8   8          column if the answer is more than 9.
```

Line up the decimal point in the answer.

Q What is 12.4 × 6.3?

A	0.7812		D	781.2
B	7.812		E	7812
C	78.12			

Method

1) In each answer option, the <u>numbers</u> are the <u>same</u>, but the decimal point is in a <u>different place</u>.

2) This means you can <u>estimate</u> the answer by <u>rounding</u> the two numbers in the calculation to the <u>nearest whole number</u>, then <u>multiplying</u> them together.

> 12.4 is rounded down to 12.   6.3 is rounded down to 6. $12 \times 6 = 72$

3) The estimated answer is <u>72</u>. The only option that is <u>near</u> to 72 is <u>78.12</u> — option C. 78.12 must be the <u>exact answer</u>.

Q 526 × 24 = 12 624

This is a number fact.

What is 526 × 12?

Quick Method

1) Use the <u>number fact</u> to help you work out the answer to the question.

2) 12 is <u>half</u> of 24. So the answer to <u>526 × 12</u> will be <u>half</u> of the answer to <u>526 × 24</u>.

> Half of 12 624 = 6312 ⟹ 526 × 12 = 6312

Written Method

1) An alternative method would be to use <u>long multiplication</u>.

2) Line the numbers up in <u>columns</u> and put the <u>bigger number</u> on top.

3) Multiply <u>each digit</u> in the bigger number with the <u>units</u> and <u>tens</u> of the smaller number:

Multiply each digit by 2.

Write the answer here.

$$\begin{array}{r} 5\ 2\ 6 \\ \times\ \ \ \ 1\ 2 \\ \hline 1\ 0\ 5\ 2 \\ {\scriptstyle 1} \end{array}$$

Then, multiply each number by 10.

Write the answer on the line below.

$$\begin{array}{r} 5\ 2\ 6 \\ \times\ \ \ \ 1\ 2 \\ \hline 1\ 0\ 5\ 2 \\ {\scriptstyle 1} \\ 5\ 2\ 6\ 0 \end{array}$$

4) <u>Add</u> your two answers together to get the final answer.

$$\begin{array}{r} 5\ 2\ 6 \\ \times\ \ \ \ 1\ 2 \\ \hline 1\ 0\ 5\ 2 \\ {\scriptstyle 1} \\ +\ 5\ 2\ 6\ 0 \\ \hline 6\ 3\ 1\ 2 \\ {\scriptstyle 1} \end{array}$$

You may have been taught a different method for written multiplication. That's fine — just use whichever one works best for you.

Section Two — Working with Numbers

> Q 230 × 44 = 10 120
>
> What is 2.3 × 4.4?

Method

1) Start by finding the <u>relationship</u> between the numbers in the <u>number fact</u> and the numbers in the <u>question</u>.

> 230 ÷ 100 = 2.3. So, 2.3 is 100 times smaller than 230.
> 44 ÷ 10 = 4.4. So, 4.4 is 10 times smaller than 44.

2) Use this to <u>work out</u> the <u>relationship</u> between the answer to the number fact and the answer to the question.

> 10 × 100 = 1000. So, the answer is 1000 times smaller than the answer to the number fact.

3) <u>Divide</u> the answer of the <u>number fact</u> by <u>1000</u> to work out the answer to the question.

> 10 120 ÷ 1000 = 10.12

There's more about how to divide by 10, 100 or 1000 on page 24.

Tips and Tricks for Multiplication Questions

If a question gives you a number fact, it's a pretty big clue that there's a quick way to work out the answer. Look closely at how the numbers in the number fact are related to the numbers in the question.

Practice Questions

1) 3.5 × 7.9 = 27.65
   What is 350 × 79?

2) What is 6.9 × 8.2?
   A 64.40   **B** 48.18   **C** 45.95   **D** 56.58   **E** 72.52

3) Each bookshelf in a library can hold 18 books.
   How many books can be held on 53 bookshelves?

Division

Division is the opposite of multiplication — you're splitting a number into groups.

Warm-Up Activity

1) Open up your money box (or find some counters). <u>Count</u> how many coins you have.
2) Start by <u>dividing</u> the coins into <u>groups of 5</u>. Count how many groups there are and make a note of the <u>remainder</u> if there is one.
3) Then do the same again with groups of <u>6</u>, <u>7</u> and <u>8</u>.

11+ Style Questions

> **Q** Each guinea pig cage holds 3 guinea pigs.
>
> How many cages would 124 guinea pigs need?

Quick Method

1) You need to <u>divide</u> 124 by 3, but 3 isn't a <u>factor</u> of 124.
2) <u>Partition</u> 124 into two numbers that are <u>easier</u> to work with. You need to find a number that's close to 124 and is a multiple of 3. You could split 124 into <u>120</u> and <u>4</u>.
3) Start by working out how many cages you'd need for <u>120 guinea pigs</u>.

> Using your 3 times table, you know that $12 \div 3 = 4$.
> 120 is 10 times bigger than 12, so $120 \div 3 = 40$.

4) Next, work out how many cages you'd need for the <u>remaining 4 guinea pigs</u>. Then <u>add</u> your two answers <u>together</u>.

> $4 \div 3 = 1$ remainder 1 $40 + 1$ remainder $1 = 41$ remainder 1

5) You still have a <u>remainder of 1</u> — so if you just have 41 cages there will be 1 poor guinea pig <u>without</u> a cage. You need <u>42 cages</u> so that every guinea pig has a cage.

Written Method

1) You can also use a written method to divide 124 by 3.

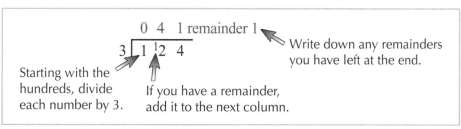

2) 41 cages will leave one extra guinea pig without a cage, so the answer must be <u>42</u>.

Emily ran for a distance of 2123 metres. It took her 9 minutes.
To the nearest whole metre, how many metres did she run per minute?

Method

1) You need to <u>divide</u> the <u>total distance</u> Emily ran by the <u>length of time</u> it took her.

$$0\ 2\ 3\ 5 \text{ remainder } 8$$

Divide each $9\overline{)2\ ^2 1\ ^3 2\ ^5 3}$ Remember to include
number by 9.   the remainder.

2) The question asks for the answer to the <u>nearest whole number</u>.
So, 235 remainder 8 should be <u>rounded up</u> to <u>236 metres</u>.

If the remainder is greater than half of the number you're dividing by, it should be rounded up. If it's less, it should be rounded down.

 What is 12.5 divided by 5?

Method

1) First, <u>convert</u> the decimal number into a <u>whole number</u> — this makes it <u>easier</u> to divide.

Multiply 12.5 by 10 to make a whole number. $12.5 \times 10 = 125$.

2) Then, find the <u>answer</u> to the <u>division</u>.

Find $125 \div 5$. Partition 125 into $100 + 25$ and divide each bit separately.
$100 \div 5 = 20$, $25 \div 5 = 5$. So $125 \div 5 = 20 + 5 = 25$.

3) Because you <u>multiplied 12.5 by 10</u> at the beginning, you've got to <u>divide</u> your answer <u>by 10</u>.

$25 \div 10 = 2.5$, so 12.5 divided by $5 = 2.5$

 Libby divides a number by a smaller number. Her answer has a remainder of 7.
Which of these numbers could Libby have divided by?

     A 8   B 4   C 6   D 5   E 7

Method

There's <u>no clear method</u> to follow here — you need to think about it logically:

To get a remainder of 7, Libby can't have divided by a number less than 7, otherwise
it could've been divided again. E.g. 4 would go into 7 once, giving a remainder of 3.

If Libby had divided by 7, then there wouldn't have been a remainder at all (because $7 \div 7 = 1$).

Libby must have divided by a number greater than 7. So the answer must be 8 — option A.

Q 3150 ÷ 9 = 350

What is 9450 ÷ 9?

This is similar to the method you used to answer the number fact question on page 27.

Quick Method

1) Use the <u>number fact</u> to help you work out the answer to the question.

2) See if you can spot how the numbers in the two calculations are <u>related to each other</u>. 9450 is <u>three times larger</u> than 3150. So, the answer to 9450 ÷ 9 will be <u>three times larger</u> than 350.

You could work this out by doing 300 × 3 and then 50 × 3. Then add the answers together. → 350 × 3 = 1050 ⟶ 9450 ÷ 9 = 1050

Written Method

1) You could use a <u>written method</u> to divide 9450 by 9.

2) Write out the division and divide <u>each number</u> in 9450 by 9:

```
        1 0 5 0
Divide each  9 ⟌ 9 4 ⁴5 0
number by 9.
```
← The answer is 1050.

Tips and Tricks for Division Questions

It's not always obvious how you should work out the answer to division questions. Think carefully about what the question is asking you to do — sometimes you'll need to partition a larger number into smaller chunks that are easier to work with.

Practice Questions

1) What is 8.8 ÷ 4?

2) A soft toy costs £1.30. How many soft toys can you buy with £14.50?

3) 19 200 ÷ 16 = 1200. What is 19 200 ÷ 4?
   A 600   **B** 2400   **C** 4800   **D** 7200   **E** 9600

4) Each level on a computer game takes 8 minutes to complete.
   If Jamil spent 264 minutes playing the computer game, how many levels does he complete?

Section Two — Working with Numbers

Algebra

Algebra isn't as scary as it sounds. Learn how it works and then practise, practise, practise...

Warm-Up Activity

Fill in the boxes so that the calculations are correct.

☐ × 6 = 48

☐ − 19 = 43

☐ × 5 = 40

84 ÷ ☐ = 7

46 + ☐ = 73

34 − 16 = ☐

Algebra is using Letters to Represent Numbers

1) Algebra uses <u>letters</u> to <u>represent</u> numbers that you don't know.

This is called an algebraic equation. $4 + x = 9$

x represents a number that you don't know.
When you add 4 to x you get 9. $4 + 5 = 9$, so $x = 5$.

2) Algebra <u>doesn't</u> use <u>multiplication signs</u> before letters.
You just write the number <u>next to</u> the letter. For example:

| $3x$ means $3 \times x$ | $2ab$ means $2 \times a \times b$ | $\frac{1}{2}x$ means $\frac{1}{2} \times x$ |

3) A <u>letter</u> written <u>over</u> a <u>number</u> means that you have to <u>divide</u> by that number. For example: → $\frac{x}{8}$ means $x \div 8$

4) Algebraic expressions also use <u>square numbers</u>.
These show that a letter is <u>multiplied by itself</u>. → x^2 means $x \times x$

5) <u>Brackets</u> are used to keep parts of an expression <u>together</u>.
You should always work out the part in brackets <u>first</u>. For example:

$3(a + b)$ means $(a + b) + (a + b) + (a + b)$

Work out the part in brackets first $(a + b)$, and then find 3 lots of the answer.

BODMAS is Really Important

Operations are things like ×, ÷, + and −.

1) <u>BODMAS</u> tells you the <u>order</u> in which <u>operations</u> should be done.

BODMAS = Brackets, Other, Division, Multiplication, Addition, Subtraction

Other is things like square numbers.

2) You may have to use BODMAS when working with <u>algebraic expressions</u>.
For example, what is the value of $3(a + 5) − 7$ when a is 4?

| $3(4 + 5) − 7$ | $(4 + 5) = 9$ | $3 \times 9 = 27$ | $27 − 7 = 20$ |

Substitute a with 4 in the expression.

Start off with the bit in the brackets.

Then multiply by 3.

Then subtract 7.

Do the **Opposite Operation** to solve an **Equation**

1) The values on the <u>left</u> hand side of an equation <u>equal</u> the values on the <u>right</u> hand side. You can use this to <u>solve</u> an <u>algebraic equation</u>, and find the <u>value</u> of the letter.

2) You need to remove parts of the equation until the <u>letter</u> is left <u>on its own</u>.

3) To remove part of an equation, do the <u>opposite operation</u> to <u>both sides</u> of the equation. For example:

+ and − are opposites, and × and ÷ are opposites.

Find x when $3x + 2 = 20$.

$3x + 2 = 20$ The opposite of $+ 2$ is $- 2$,
  $- 2 \quad - 2$ so subtract 2 from both sides.

$3x = 18$ x is being multiplied by 3.
  $\div 3 \quad \div 3$ The opposite of $\times 3$ is $\div 3$, so divide by 3 on both sides.

$x = 6$ That gives you the answer — x is 6.

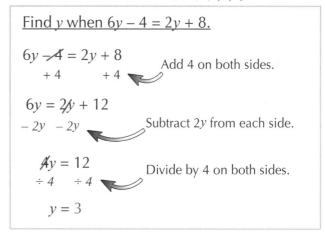

Find y when $6y - 4 = 2y + 8$.

$6y - 4 = 2y + 8$ Add 4 on both sides.
  $+ 4 \qquad + 4$

$6y = 2y + 12$
  $- 2y \quad - 2y$ Subtract $2y$ from each side.

$4y = 12$ Divide by 4 on both sides.
  $\div 4 \quad \div 4$

$y = 3$

11+ **Style** Questions

Q   A farm calculates the cost of eggs in pence (E) using this equation:

$E = 40 + 2x^2$

x is the number of eggs bought.

A man buys 9 eggs. What is the total cost in pounds?

Method

1) The man buys <u>9 eggs</u>, so <u>change x</u> in the equation to <u>9</u>.

$E = 40 + 2 \times 9^2$

2) Solve the equation <u>one part at a time</u>. Remember to follow BODMAS.

First, work out 9^2...

 $E = 40 + 2 \times 81$ $9^2 = 9 \times 9 = 81$

... then do the multiplication...

$E = 40 + 162$ $2 \times 81 = 162$

... then work out the addition to find the cost in pence...

$E = 202$ $162 + 40 = 202$

... then divide by 100 to find the cost in pounds.

$E = 202\text{p} = £2.02$ *Don't forget this last step. The question asked for the answer in pounds.*

The 'nth term' is the name given to any term in a sequence.

Q Gael uses squares to make the first three terms of a sequence.

| 1st term | 2nd term | 3rd term |

What is the correct expression for the number of squares in the *n*th term of the sequence?

A $3n - 1$ B $2n + 7$ C $3n + 6$ D $n + 3$ E $5n$

Method 1

1) You could test <u>each option</u> to find the expression which <u>works</u> for the <u>sequence</u>.

2) To test each expression, you have to <u>replace *n*</u> with the <u>term number</u> of the sequence.

3) Start with option A, <u>$3n - 1$</u>:

> For the 1st term, $3n - 1 = 3 \times 1 - 1 = 2$. The 1st term has 9 squares, so the expression is incorrect.

4) Move on to option B, <u>$2n + 7$</u>:

> For the 1st term, $2n + 7 = 2 \times 1 + 7 = 9$. This expression is correct for the 1st term.
> For the 2nd term, $2n + 7 = 2 \times 2 + 7 = 11$. The 2nd term has 12 squares — incorrect.

5) Next, try option C, <u>$3n + 6$</u>:

> For the 1st term, $3n + 6 = 3 \times 1 + 6 = 9$. This expression is correct for the 1st term.
> For the 2nd term, $3n + 6 = 3 \times 2 + 6 = 12$. It's also correct for the 2nd term.
> For the 3rd term, $3n + 6 = 3 \times 3 + 6 = 15$. Bingo — it's correct for the 3rd term as well.

6) So, you know that the <u>correct</u> answer is <u>option C</u> — you don't have to check the other options.

Method 2

1) You can <u>work out</u> the <u>expression</u> for the <u>*n*th term</u> of the sequence.

2) Look for the relationship between the <u>number of squares</u> in each term.

Term Number	1	2	3
Number of Squares	9	12	15

+3   +3

The number of squares increases by 3 between each term. The sequence is following the three times table, so you need to multiply by three in the expression.

3) <u>Start</u> your expression with '<u>$3n$</u>'.

> For the 1st term, $n = 1$. So $3n = 3 \times 1 = 3$. The table says term 1 has 9 squares.
> So if you add 6, you have made a rule that works for the 1st term of the sequence, $3n + 6$.

4) Check your expression is <u>correct</u> by testing the <u>other terms</u>.

> For the 2nd term, $3n + 6 = 3 \times 2 + 6 = 12$. For the 3rd term, $3n + 6 = 3 \times 3 + 6 = 15$.

5) The expression works for <u>all three terms</u>. So the correct answer is <u>$3n + 6$</u> — option <u>C</u>.

At a restaurant, a hamburger costs £3 and a hot dog costs £2. Which expression gives the total cost, in pounds, of buying x hamburgers and y hot dogs?

    A $2x + y$ B $5y - x$ C $3xy$ D $3x + 2y$ E $x \times y$

Method

1) Make the expression one part at a time.

2) Start by finding the cost (in pounds) of <u>x hamburgers</u>:

   | Cost of hamburgers = $3x$ | The cost of the hamburgers is the number you're buying (x) multiplied by the price (£3). So this should be written as $3x$.

3) Next, add the cost (in pounds) of <u>y hotdogs</u> to <u>complete</u> the expression:

   | $3x + 2y$ | Each hotdog costs £2, so the price of y hotdogs is $2y$ pounds.

        To find the total cost, add the cost of the hotdogs to the cost of the hamburgers.

4) That gives you the <u>finished expression</u>. The correct answer is <u>$3x + 2y$</u> — option <u>D</u>.

Tips and Tricks for Algebra Questions

When you've written an algebraic expression, you can try it out to check it's right. For the question above, imagine that you bought 1 hamburger and 1 hotdog. You know that the total cost will be £5 (£3 + £2 = £5), so make sure that your expression gives you 5 as the answer when x is 1 and y is 1.

Practice Questions

1) The cost (in pounds) of calling out an electrician (C) is shown by the equation: $C = 25 + 10h + p$ where h is the number of hours and p is the cost (in pounds) of any parts.
   What is the cost of the electrician when they work for 3 hours and need £20 worth of parts?

2) 6, 11, 16, 21
   What is the expression for the nth term of this sequence?
   A $n^2 + 5$ **B** $n + 5$ **C** $5n - 1$ **D** $5n + 5$ **E** $5n + 1$

3) The width of a room is 3 m. The length of the room is four times the width of the room. The height of the room is y m. Which of these is the correct expression for finding the volume of the room in m³?
   A $12y \times 4$ **B** $3y \times 4y$ **C** $12y + 3y$ **D** $36y$ **E** $y + 36$

           Volume is calculated by length × width × height.

Mixed Calculations

Mixed calculation questions will test all of your adding, subtracting, dividing and multiplying skills. But don't worry — there are some handy tricks you can learn to make them much easier.

Warm-Up Activity

1) Find a pack of <u>playing cards</u>.
2) Ask someone else to join you and take it in turns to pick <u>three cards</u>.
3) <u>Multiply together</u> the numbers on the <u>first two</u> cards you pick. Then <u>divide</u> the result by the number on the <u>third</u> card (Ace, Jack, Queen and King all count as 10). Give yourself 1 point if you score <u>5 or more</u>.
4) The first player to get <u>5 points</u> is the winner.

11+ Style Questions

> **Q** $42 \times 603 + 58 \times 603 =$
>
> A　1 206　　　　D　54 270
>
> B　25 326　　　　E　60 300
>
> C　34 974

Quick Method

42 and 58 are <u>both multiplied</u> by 603.
You can just add <u>42 and 58</u> and <u>multiply</u> this number by <u>603</u> to find the answer.

> $42 + 58 = 100$. So $42 \times 603 + 58 \times 603$ simplifies to 100×603.
> $100 \times 603 = 60\ 300$ — so the correct answer is option E.

Written Method

1) An alternative (but <u>slower</u>) method would be to follow the <u>BODMAS</u> rule and do each <u>multiplication before adding</u> each of the answers.

For more on BODMAS, see page 32.

2) First, calculate 42×603 and 58×603 using a <u>written method</u>.

```
      6 0 3            6 0 3
  ×     4 2        ×     5 8
  ─────────        ─────────
    1 2 0 6          4 8 2 4
                          2
  +2 4 1 2 0        +3 0 1 5 0
        1                1
  ─────────        ─────────
    2 5 3 2 6        3 4 9 7 4
```

It doesn't matter what method you use to do these multiplications — use whichever method you find easiest. See pages 26-27 for more on written multiplication.

3) Then <u>add together</u> the answers to these multiplications to find the correct answer.

```
    2 5 3 2 6
  +3 4 9 7 4
  ─────────
    6 0 3 0 0      So 42 × 603 + 58 × 603 = 60 300. The correct answer is option E.
      1 1 1 1
```

Q What is 360 ÷ (40 × 1.5)?

Method

1) Follow the <u>BODMAS</u> rule and do the calculation in <u>brackets before</u> the <u>division</u>.

> Use partitioning to find 40 × 1.5. Partition 1.5 into 1 and 0.5.
> 40 × 1 = 40, and 40 × 0.5 = 20 (it's the same as half of 40).
> Add together your results, 40 + 20 = 60.

2) Now work out <u>360 ÷ 60</u>.

> Both the numbers in the calculation end in a zero. This means you can simplify this calculation by dividing both numbers by 10. 360 ÷ 10 = 36, and 60 ÷ 10 = 6.
>
> Now your calculation is just 36 ÷ 6 = 6.

3) So the <u>answer</u> is <u>6</u>.

Tips and Tricks for Mixed Calculations

Multiplying or dividing numbers by 10, 100 or 1000 can make a calculation much easier. Remember though — if you've only simplified one of the numbers in your calculation, then you need to do the opposite function to your answer so it's correct.

Practice Questions

1) Ahmed wants to work out the cost of three oranges, two carrot cakes and one tuna roll. Which of these calculations could he do?

A 3 × 40p + 2 × £2 + 1 × £1 + 5p
B 3 × 40p + 2 × £2 + 1 × £1 − 5p
C 3 × 40p + 2 × £2 + 1 × £1 + 3p
D 3 × 40p + 2 × £2 + 1 × £1 − 6p
E 3 × 40p + 2 × £2 + 1 × £1 + 6p

Tuck Shop
Cola.......................... 69p
Squash.....................49p
Orange.....................39p
Tuna Roll..................99p
Carrot Cake............£1.99

2) Which of these calculations would give the largest answer?

A 12 × 14 + 15 − 13
B 13 × 15 + 14 − 12
C 15 × 13 + 12 − 13
D 14 × 13 + 12 − 15
E 15 × 12 + 13 − 14

Word Problems

Word problems can be tricky — you need to read them very carefully to work out what they're asking. Then you can work out the best way to answer them quickly and correctly.

11+ *Style* Questions

 A zoo has a total of 39 parrots and peacocks.
Which of these statements cannot be true?
A There are more parrots than peacocks in the zoo.
B There are more peacocks than parrots in the zoo.
C There are three more parrots than peacocks in the zoo.
D There are seven more peacocks than parrots in the zoo.
E There are twelve more parrots than peacocks in the zoo.

Method

You need to <u>test each sentence</u>.

A	The total number of parrots and peacocks in the zoo is odd (39). An odd number can't be divided by two to give two equal whole numbers, so there must be more of one bird than the other, e.g. there could be 20 parrots and 19 peacocks — so this could be true.
B	This could be true for the same reason that A could be true.
C	The quickest way to work out if this is true is to use the properties of odd and even numbers. The total number of birds is odd, which means the sum of the number of parrots and peacocks must be an odd number added to an even number. The difference between an odd and an even number is always odd. 3 is an odd number, and so this could be true.
	You could also calculate whether two whole numbers with a difference of 3 add to make 39. Subtract 3 from the total number of birds (39 – 3 = 36). Then divide 36 by 2 (36 ÷ 2 = 18). So you have two sets of 18 — add 3 to one of these to give you 21 and 18. These are two numbers that add up to 39, but have a difference of 3 — so this could be true.
D	The difference between the numbers of parrots and peacocks is odd, and 7 is an odd number — so it could be true.
	Or subtract 7 from 39 (39 – 7 = 32). Then divide 32 by 2 (32 ÷ 2 = 16). So you have two sets of 16 — add 7 to one of these to give you 23 and 16. These are two numbers that add up to 39, but have a difference of 7 — so this could be true.
E	12 is even, but the difference between the numbers of parrots and peacocks must be odd — so this cannot be true.
	Or subtract 12 from 39 (39 – 12 = 27). Then divide 27 by 2 (27 ÷ 2 = 13.5). So you have two sets of 13.5 — add 12 to one of these to give you 25.5 and 13.5. These two numbers do add up to 39, but you can't have half a peacock or parrot, so this cannot be true.

Beanthwaite School ordered 6 boxes of rulers in March and 4 boxes in April.
Each box contained 130 rulers.
How many rulers did the school order in total?

Method

1) Work out the total number of boxes ordered.

> 6 boxes were ordered in March and 4 were ordered in April, so 6 + 4 = 10.

2) Multiply the total number of boxes by the number of rulers in each box.

> 10 × 130 = 1300 rulers in total.

 Raisa went to a restaurant with two friends.
They ordered from the menu: 3 plates of
lasagne, 2 soups and 4 lemonades.

Raisa pays with a £50 note.

How much change should she receive?

Luigi's Restaurant	
Lemonade................	90p
Soup.....................	£2.50
Carbonara..............	£7.50
Pizza....................	£6.00
Lasagne................	£8.50

Method

1) Work out how much each item will cost. Make sure that all the amounts are in pounds.

> 3 plates of lasagne is 3 × £8.50. | 2 soups is 2 × £2.50. | 4 lemonades is 4 × 90p.
> Split £8.50 into £8 and £0.50 | 2 × £2.5 = £5.00 | 4 × 90p = 360p
> 3 × £8 = £24, 3 × £0.50 = £1.50 | | 360p = £3.60
> So 3 × £8.50 = £24 + £1.50 = £25.50

2) Now find the total cost of all of the items.

> You could use partitioning to find the total amount.
> Add up all the pounds. 25 + 5 + 3 = £33.
> Add up all the pence. 50 + 60 = 110p = £1.10
> Now add them together. £33 + £1.10 = £34.10

For questions like this where you have lots of numbers to work with, it's helpful to make notes on some rough paper so you don't forget anything.

3) Now find the difference between the total cost of the items and £50.

> You can count on from £34.10 to £50.
> Count on to £35. £34.10 + 90p = £35
> Then count on to £50. £35 + £15 = £50
> Add the two numbers to find the difference. £15 + 90p = £15.90.

4) So the answer is £15.90.

Q A number is first multiplied by 3 and then squared.
The number ends up as 36.
What was the number at the start?

A 2   C 6   E 10
B 4   D 8

Method

You know the <u>final answer</u> — to find the <u>number at the start</u> you need to work
<u>backwards</u> through the calculation given in the question. You can do this in <u>two steps</u>.

> 1) The number at the end is 36. To get 36 a number was squared.
> The only number that could be squared to give 36 is 6.

> 2) To get 6 a number was multiplied by 3.
> To find the missing number you just divide 6 by 3. $6 \div 3 = 2$.

Q A drinks company makes 250 litres of tropical
punch each week. Look at the ingredients
used to make the punch.

The company sells the tropical
punch in 50 litre barrels.

Tropical Punch	
Mango Juice	95.4 l
Orange Juice	45.5 l
Pineapple Juice	62.1 l
Apple Juice	47 l

How many litres of orange juice are in one barrel of tropical punch?

A 3.4 l   C 18.0 l   E 11.6 l
B 8.5 l   D 9.1 l

Method

1) First you need to work out what <u>fraction</u> of <u>250 l</u> makes up <u>1 barrel</u> of <u>tropical punch</u>.

> 1 barrel = 50 l. $250 \div 50 = 5$, so 1 barrel is $\frac{1}{5}$ of 250 l.

2) There are <u>45.5 l</u> of orange juice in <u>250 l</u> of tropical punch,
so you need to find $\frac{1}{5}$ of 45.5 l.

> To find $\frac{1}{5}$ of 45.5 you need to divide 45.5 by 5.
>
> There are options to choose from, so you could make an estimate.
> $45 \div 5 = 9$, so the answer to $45.5 \div 5$ will be a little greater than 9.
> Option D is 9.1 l — so this is the correct answer.

Q A counter is worth 5 points and has a diameter of 3.5 cm.
A row of counters was lined up in a game, with each counter
touching the next. The values on the line of counters added
up to 1500 points.

Find the length of the row of
counters, in metres.

3.5 cm

Method

1) Work out how many <u>counters</u> there are in <u>total</u>.

> There are 1500 points worth of 5 point counters.
> So the total number of counters is 1500 ÷ 5.
> 1500 is 100 times larger than 15, so 1500 ÷ 5 must be 100 times larger than 15 ÷ 5.
> 15 ÷ 5 = 3. So 1500 ÷ 5 = 100 × 3 = 300

2) Now find the <u>length</u> of the <u>line</u> of <u>counters</u>.

> Each counter is 3.5 cm in diameter, and there are 300 in total — so work out 300 × 3.5.
> Partition 3.5 into 3 and 0.5.
> 300 × 3 = 900. 300 × 0.5 = 150 (it's the same as half of 300).
> Then add up the result. 900 + 150 = 1050 cm.

3) Don't forget to <u>convert</u> your <u>answer</u> into <u>metres</u>: <u>1050 cm</u> ÷ 100 = <u>10.5 m</u>.

Practice Questions

1) A bunch of seven tulips costs £4.50. A bunch of six roses costs £3.50.
Lena wants 42 tulips and 42 roses. How much does she need to pay?

   A £24.50
   B £147.00
   C £189.00
   D £27.00
   E £51.50

2) Benni buys 5 sandwiches. He pays with a £10 note
and gets £1.50 change. How much is one sandwich?

3) Simone made bracelets to sell. Each bracelet cost her 20p to make and
she sold them for 50p each. She sold 57 bracelets in total. How much
money did she make, after she subtracted the cost of making the bracelets?

Data Tables

Data is just any set of facts or information. It's often easier to understand and use if you organise it into a table, particularly if there's a lot of it.

Warm-Up Activity

Roll a dice 30 times. <u>Record</u> the number you roll in a <u>frequency table</u> like the one on the right. <u>How many times</u> did you roll <u>each number</u>?

Number on dice	Tally	Frequency
1	IIII	4
2	LHT I	6
3	LHT	5

Frequency just means how many times something happens.

11+ Style Questions

Q Ryan does a survey to find out how much the shops in his town charge for a can of cola. He groups his results into price bands and puts them in this table.
Which of these statements is definitely true?

Price	Frequency
50p – 59p	4
60p – 69p	10
70p – 79p	12
80p – 89p	8
90p – £1.00	6

A The most expensive can of cola Ryan found costs £1.00.

B Ryan recorded the prices of 42 cans of cola.

C More than half of the cans of cola cost between 70p and 79p each.

D Three-quarters of the cans of cola cost less than 80p each.

E More than half of the cans of cola cost 70p or more each.

Method

Look at <u>each option</u> and work out whether it's <u>definitely true</u>.

A	The table only tells you that the most expensive can of cola is between 90p and £1.00. It might not be exactly £1.00 though — so you don't know if the statement is definitely true.
B	To find the total number of cans of cola, add up all the frequencies in the table. 4 + 10 + 12 + 8 + 6 = 40 — so the statement isn't true.
C	Half of the total number of cans is 40 ÷ 2 = 20. There are only 12 cola cans in the 70p –79p price band — so the statement isn't true.
D	One quarter of the total number of cans is 40 ÷ 4 = 10, so three quarters is 30. Add together the first three rows to find the number of cans that cost less than 80p: 4 + 10 + 12 = 26. 26 isn't three-quarters of the total number of cans — so the statement isn't true.
E	Add together the last three rows of the table to find the total number of cans that cost 70p or more = 12 + 8 + 6 = 26. This is more than half of the total number of cans (20) — so this statement is true. E is the correct answer.

Q Years 5 and 6 are having a party. They all choose between meat pie and cheese pie. This table shows some of their choices. How many children are there in Year 5?

	Year 5	Year 6	**Total**
Meat pie		12	
Cheese pie	21		39
Total			64

Method

1) This is a <u>two-way table</u>. There's a total for each row and column.

	Year 5	Year 6	**Total**
Meat pie		12	
Cheese pie	21		39
Total			64

Total number of cheese pies eaten.

Total number of pies eaten and the total number of children in Year 5 and Year 6.

This is the space for the number of children in Year 5.

Number of meat pies eaten by Year 6.

2) You don't have enough <u>information</u> to work out how many children there are in year 5 straight away — you need to <u>fill in</u> some of the other <u>empty</u> boxes first.

	Year 5	Year 6	**Total**
Meat pie	**13**	12	**25**
Cheese pie	21		39
Total			64

First find out how many meat pies were eaten in total.
Total number – total cheese pie eaters = 64 – 39 = 25

Now you can find out how many meat pies Year 5 ate.
Total meat pie eaters – Year 6 meat pie eaters = 25 – 12 = 13

3) <u>Add</u> the numbers in the <u>Year 5 column</u> of the table to find the number of children in Year 5.

Year 5 children = Year 5 meat + Year 5 cheese
pie eaters pie eaters
= 13 + 21 = 34

	Year 5	Year 6	**Total**
Meat pie	**13**	12	**25**
Cheese pie	21		39
Total	**34**		64

Practice Questions

1) The table on the right shows the numbers of DVDs owned by some children. How many children own more than 15 DVDs?

A 9 **B** 19 **C** 28 **D** 27 **E** 13

DVDs	Frequency
0 – 5	14
6 – 10	13
11 – 15	9
16 – 20	13
21 – 25	6

2) The table below shows an order form for some pantomime tickets. Some boxes have been left empty. Calculate the cost of a senior citizen ticket.

Ticket	Price	Number needed	Total cost
Child	£5	32	£160
Adult	£8	4	£32
Senior Citizen		3	
		Booking Fee	£2.50
		Amount to pay	**£212.50**

Section Four — Data Handling

Displaying Data

Charts and graphs aren't just an excuse for a bit of colouring. They're a really important way of showing data — they can help you understand information at a glance.

Bar Charts Make it Easy to **Compare** things

Bar charts have two axes. The horizontal axis is called the x-axis.
The vertical axis is called the y-axis — it usually shows the frequency.

The height of each bar on this chart tells you how many games of chess were played on each day. Just read across from the top of the bar to the number on the left.

E.g. this bar chart shows there were 6 games of chess played on Friday.

Line Graphs Often Show things that **Change over Time**

1) Line graphs show you how one thing (shown on the y-axis) changes as another thing changes (shown on the x-axis).

2) Time is often on the x-axis. For example, this graph shows how the temperature in an oven changes over time.

Between 2:30 and 3:30 the graph is flat — so the temperature stays the same.

Between 2:00 and 2:30 the graph slopes upwards — so the temperature is increasing.

Between 3:30 and 5:00 the graph slopes downwards — so the temperature is decreasing.

3) Here's how to read off a value from a line graph, e.g. the temperature at 3:45 from this line graph.

Step 1 — Find 3:45 on the x-axis. Follow a line straight up to the graph line.

Step 2 — Now follow a line straight across to the y-axis.

Step 3 — Read the temperature value from the y-axis — 140 °C.

Pictograms use **Symbols** to Show Frequency

1) In pictograms, simple pictures show numbers of things or how often something happens.

2) The key is really important — it tells you how many things each picture stands for.

This pictogram shows how many
chess games were played each day. ⟹

This is the key. It tells you
that one complete symbol
represents 2 games.

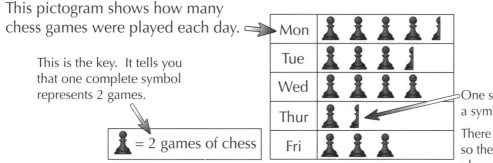

♟ = 2 games of chess

One symbol = 2 games, so half
a symbol = 2 ÷ 2 = 1 game.

There are 1½ symbols for Thursday,
so there were 2 + 1 = 3 games
played on Thursday.

Pie Charts Show Things as **Proportions**

*Proportion just means the
fraction of the total amount.*

1) Each 'slice' of a pie chart is called a sector. You can work out the number
of things shown by each sector on a pie chart.

2) For example, the pie charts below show what 60 four-year-old boys said they
wanted to be when they grow up. You can find how many boys said each
thing by working out what fraction a sector is of the whole pie.

The 'Fireman' sector is $\frac{1}{4}$ of the pie.

You know that there are 60 boys in total,
so find $\frac{1}{4}$ of 60.

60 ÷ 4 = 15 boys said fireman.

You can also use the number of degrees that make up a sector to work
out how many boys said each thing.

The 'Pirate' sector has an angle of 60°.

The pie chart is a circle, so the total angle of all the sectors is 360°.

The fraction of the whole pie made up by the pirate sector is $\frac{60°}{360°}$ $\frac{1}{6}$

So the number of boys that want to be a pirate is $\frac{1}{6}$ of 60 = 60 ÷ 6 = 10.

11+ *Style* Questions

Q The bar chart shows the scores a class of students got in a maths test.

Which other group of test marks add up to the same number of students that got 41-50 marks?

A Less than 41   C 11-20

B 51-60   D 31-40 and 11-20   E 51-60 and 0-10

Method

1) There are <u>no numbers</u> on the *y*-axis, so you <u>can't calculate</u> which answer is correct. You need to go through the options and <u>visually compare</u> the heights of the bars.

> A   This is the height of the 0-10, 11-20, 21-30 and 31-40 bars added together. This would add up to make a much greater number of students than the 41-50 bar — incorrect.
>
> B   The 51-60 bar on its own is a smaller number than the 41-50 bar — incorrect.
>
> C   The 11-20 bar on its own is a much smaller number than the 41-50 bar — incorrect.
>
> D   The height of the 31-40 bar added to the height of the 11-20 bar would make the same number of students as the 41-50 bar — correct.

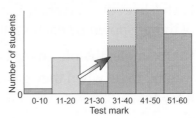

2) <u>D</u> is the <u>correct answer</u> — you don't need to look at option E.

Q A chef uses 35 oz of pastry to make some apple pies.

She needs to use 4 apples for every 400 g of pastry.

Use the graph to work out how many apples she needs if she uses all the pastry to make apple pies.

Method

1) <u>Read off</u> how much 35 oz of pastry is <u>in grams</u> from the graph.

> 35 oz = 1000 g.

2) Find the amount of pastry used for <u>1 apple</u>.

> For 400 g of pastry you need 4 apples.
> So she uses 400 ÷ 4 = 100 g of pastry for 1 apple.

3) She needs <u>1 apple</u> for every <u>100 g</u> of pastry and she's using <u>1000 g</u> of pastry.

> 1000 ÷ 100 = 10 — she needs 10 apples.

Section Four — Data Handling

Q The pictogram shows the number of differently shaped sweets in a bag.

How many more animal shaped sweets than fruit shaped sweets are there in the bag?

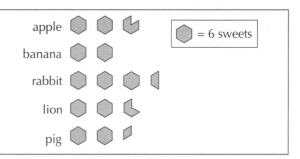

Method

1) First work out <u>how many</u> sweets are <u>animal shaped</u> (i.e. either a rabbit, a lion or a pig).

> There are 7 whole symbols for the animal sweets. $7 \times 6 = 42$ sweets.
> The rabbit shape also has $\frac{3}{6}$ of a symbol on the end = 3 sweets, the lion shape has $\frac{4}{6}$ of a symbol on the end = 4 sweets and the pig shape has $\frac{2}{6}$ of a symbol on the end = 2 sweets.
> Add these together to get the total number of animal shaped sweets. $42 + 3 + 4 + 2 = 51$ sweets.

2) Now use the same method to work out <u>how many fruit sweets</u> there are.

> There are 4 whole symbols for fruit shaped sweets. $4 \times 6 = 24$ sweets. The apple shape also has $\frac{5}{6}$ of a symbol on the end = 5 sweets. Total number of fruit shaped sweets = $24 + 5 = 29$ sweets.

3) Then <u>subtract</u> to find the <u>difference</u> between the two.

> There are $51 - 29 = 22$ more animal shaped sweets than fruit shaped sweets.

Q The table shows the ingredients in 300 ml of a salad dressing. Ben wants to draw a pie chart to show the proportion of each ingredient in the dressing.

What angle would the olive oil sector of the pie chart have?

Ingredient	Amount
Olive oil	50 ml
Vinegar	200 ml
Lemon juice	50 ml

Method

1) First find what <u>fraction</u> of the dressing is made up of olive oil.

> 50 ml out of 300 ml is olive oil.
> The fraction of the total dressing that's olive oil is $\frac{50}{300}$ $\frac{1}{6}$
>
> *Divide the numerator and the denominator by 50 to simplify.*

2) The <u>total angles</u> in a pie chart are <u>360°</u>, so find $\frac{1}{6}$ of 360°.

> $\frac{1}{6}$ of 360° = 360° ÷ 6 = 60°.

Practice Question

1) A class of children were asked what their favourite colour is.
   Two children chose brown. This was represented on a pie chart
   by a 20° sector. How many children are in the class?

Section Four — Data Handling

Mode, Median, Mean and Range

Mode, median and mean are all types of average. An average is one number which summarises a whole set of numbers. The range isn't an average — it's just the difference between the highest and lowest value in a set.

Learn How to Find the **Mode**, **Median** and **Mean**

The **Mode** is the **Most Common** Value

1) If you write out all the numbers in a data set, the <u>mode</u> is the value that appears <u>most often</u>.

2) So in this list of shoe sizes: | 4, 4, 4.5, 4, 4, 5 | 4 is the mode.

3) If all the values in a data set are <u>different</u> there is <u>no mode</u>.

The **Median** is the **Middle** Value

1) If you write out all the numbers in a data set in <u>order of size</u>, the <u>median</u> is the value that appears <u>exactly in the middle</u> of the list.

2) If there's an <u>odd number</u> of values in the data set, then you can just <u>read off</u> the middle value. → | 10, 13, 27, 29, 36, 42, 69 |

3) If there's an <u>even number</u> of values in the data set, then you need to calculate the number that's <u>halfway between</u> the two middle values (if they're both the <u>same value</u>, then just read off that value). | 2, 4, 7, 8, 11, 14 |

7 and 8 are the middle values, so the median is halfway between them — 7 + 8 = 15. 15 ÷ 2 = 7.5

The **Mean** Involves **Adding** and **Dividing**

1) To work out the <u>mean</u>: →
- <u>Add</u> up all the numbers in the data set.
- <u>Divide</u> the total by <u>how many</u> numbers there are.

2) So the mean of the data set on the <u>right</u> is (13 + 8 + 7 + 4 + 11 + 2) ÷ 6 = 7.5. | 13, 8, 7, 4, 11, 2 |

Range = Biggest Number – Smallest Number

1) The <u>range</u> is just the <u>difference</u> between the <u>biggest</u> and <u>smallest</u> numbers.

2) So for the data set on the <u>right</u>, the range = 13 – 2 = 11. | 13, 8, 7, 4, 11, 2 |

11+ Style Questions

Q The bar chart shows five children's marks in three tests.

Which child's marks had the greatest range?

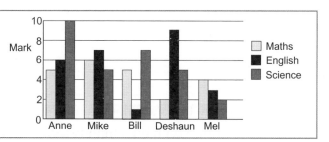

Method

1) <u>Subtract</u> each child's <u>lowest mark</u> from their <u>highest mark</u> to find each range.

Anne: 10 − 5 = 5	Mike: 7 − 5 = 2	Bill: 7 − 1 = 6
Deshaun: 9 − 2 = 7	Mel: 4 − 2 = 2	

2) <u>Compare</u> the ranges — the biggest is 7, so the answer is Deshaun.

Q Derek has a set of five numbers. He calculates that the mean of his numbers is 11.5.

8	13	18	7.5	11

He forgets one of his numbers.

The mean of the four numbers he can remember is 12.5.

Which number has he forgotten?

Method

1) First work out the <u>total</u> of the numbers <u>he can remember</u>.

If the mean of the four numbers he can remember is 12.5, he must have divided a number by 4 to get 12.5. So multiply 12.5 by 4 to find the total. $12.5 \times 4 = 50$.

2) Then work out the <u>total</u> of the <u>original five numbers</u>.

$8 + 13 + 18 + 7.5 + 11 = 57.5$

3) <u>Subtract</u> the total of the four numbers he can <u>remember</u> from the <u>original total</u>.

$57.5 - 50 = 7.5$ — the number he forgot was 7.5.

Practice Question

1) The data set on the right shows how many tea bags were used in the Smith household each day. Which of the following is correct?

A Mean = 21, Mode = 20, Median = 17, Range = 1
B Mean = 21, Mode = 17, Median = 22, Range = 9
C Mean = 20.5, Mode = 17, Median = 17, Range = 9
D Mean = 21, Mode = 20, Median = 22, Range = 4
E Mean = 20.5, Mode = 17, Median = 22, Range = 9

Mon	Tue	Wed	Thur	Fri
22	23	17	17	26

Section Four — Data Handling

Misleading Data

People often use data to try to prove a point they're making. However, you have to think really hard about data to make sure it's not being twisted to make you believe something that's not true.

Warm-Up Activity

See if you can spot why this statement is <u>misleading</u>:

Sprouts are <u>more popular</u> with girls than boys. <u>One-quarter</u> of ten year old girls <u>like</u> sprouts, whereas <u>75%</u> of ten year old boys <u>don't like</u> them.

11+ Style Questions

> *Children prefer playing computer games to playing sport.*
>
> A group of school children were asked, 'What is your favourite weekend activity?'. 20% of them said 'playing computer games', while only 1 in 4 children said their favourite activity was 'playing sport'.

Why is this newspaper article misleading?

A The article doesn't say what other activities the children picked.

B According to the numbers given in the article, more children said they liked playing sport than playing computer games.

C The article doesn't tell you how many boys and girls were in the group asked.

D The figures in the article show that fewer children chose sport than computer games.

E The article doesn't tell you what sports or computer games the children like to play.

Method

1) <u>Read the article</u> and work out what the article is <u>claiming</u> to be <u>true</u>.

> The headline says that children prefer playing computer games to playing sport.

2) Look <u>carefully</u> at any <u>figures</u> you're given, to see if they <u>back up</u> what the article is <u>claiming</u>. Put the figures into the <u>same form</u> (e.g. fractions, decimals or percentages) to <u>compare</u> them.

> 20% of children said their favourite activity was playing computer games.
> 1 in 4 children said playing sport — which is the same as 25%.
>
> 25% is greater than 20%, so more children said playing sport than playing computer games.

3) Look at the <u>options</u> to see which one is <u>correct</u>.

> Options A, C, and E are all true, but they don't mean that the article is misleading.
> Option D is incorrect — the figures show that more children chose sport than computer games.
> Option B is correct. The article is misleading because it says that fewer people picked sport than computer games, when the figures show that more people picked sport than computer games.

Q This graph is used to show the increase in the number of chickens eaten by the population of a country between 2010 and 2011.

Why is the graph misleading?

A Only two years are shown on the graph.

B The scale on the vertical axis is uneven.

C The graph doesn't show how many turkeys were eaten.

D We are not told which country the data is about.

E The chicken picture for 2011 is more than double the area of the 2010 picture.

Method

1) The graph is a type of bar chart, but it uses <u>pictures</u> of chickens instead of bars. The <u>height</u> of each picture tells you how many chickens were eaten.

> It shows that 30 million chickens were eaten in 2010, and 60 million chickens were eaten in 2011.

2) Look at each answer and decide if it's a <u>good reason</u> why the graph is misleading.

> A: The graph is only about 2010 and 2011, so it's not misleading that only two years are shown.
>
> B: This isn't true. The values are evenly spaced.
>
> C: It doesn't matter how many turkeys are eaten — the graph is about chickens.
>
> D: You haven't been led to believe that the data is about anywhere in particular, so this isn't the answer.
>
> E: From reading the graph you know that about twice as many chickens were eaten in 2011 than 2010. The trouble is, the area of the chicken for 2011 is about 4 times as big as the area of the chicken for 2010. This means that at a glance, the graph makes it look like many more chickens got eaten in 2011 compared to 2010 than actually were. E is the correct answer.

Tips and Tricks for Misleading Graph questions

Watch out for graphs that have a *y*-axis that doesn't start at zero (shown by a zigzag line).

E.g. These bar charts show the same data, but the second one makes the difference in the heights of the bars look much bigger than the first.

Practice Question

1) A newspaper report with a graph has the headline:
   Sales of pencils plummet. Why is the report misleading?

   A There are no crosses on the graph to mark the plotted points.

   B The graph does not show how many pens were sold.

   C The *y*-axis doesn't start on zero so it makes the drop in sales look worse than it is.

   D The graph doesn't show what happened before 2002.

   E The pencil manufacturers want you to go and buy more pencils.

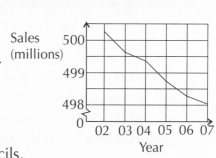

Probability

Probability is a measure of how likely something is to happen.

Warm-Up Activity

Think of some <u>events</u> that are:
1) Almost <u>certain</u> to happen.
2) As <u>likely</u> to happen as <u>not</u> to happen.
3) Almost <u>certainly not</u> going to happen.

The **Probability Scale** goes from **0 to 1**

1) If something is <u>impossible</u>, the probability is <u>0</u>. If something is <u>certain</u>, the probability is <u>1</u>.

2) Everything else falls somewhere <u>in between</u>.

A coin landing on heads.

0   **Even**   1

Scoring 6 when you roll a dice.   Tuesday will come after Monday.

Probabilities are Usually **Written** Using **Fractions**

1) All probabilities can be written as a <u>fraction</u>.

> For example, the <u>probability of rolling a 6</u> on a dice is $\frac{1}{6}$.
>
> The <u>denominator</u> usually tells you <u>how many possible things</u> might happen. There are six possible numbers you can throw on a dice, so the denominator is 6.
>
> $\frac{1}{6}$
>
> There is only one 6 on a dice, so the <u>numerator</u> is a 1 — only <u>one</u> of the <u>six</u> possible outcomes is to roll a 6.

Have a look back at pages 14-16 for more on fractions.

2) Probabilities are usually given as a fraction using the <u>lowest numbers</u> you can. <u>Divide</u> the numerator and the denominator by <u>the same number</u> to <u>simplify</u> a fraction.

> This spinner is split into <u>eight equal sections</u>.
>
> <u>Two</u> of the sections are <u>green</u> — so the chance of the spinner landing on a green section is $\frac{2}{8}$.
>
> You can <u>simplify</u> this fraction by <u>dividing</u> the numerator and denominator by 2. So the <u>chance</u> of the spinner landing on <u>a green section</u> is $\frac{1}{4}$.

$\div 2$

$\frac{2}{8}$ $\frac{1}{4}$

$\div 2$

3) Probabilities can also be given as <u>percentages</u> or <u>decimals</u>.
E.g. a chance of $\frac{1}{4}$ is the same as a chance of <u>0.25</u> or <u>25%</u>.

11+ Style Questions

Q There are 24 bags of crisps in a cupboard.
The table shows how many bags of each flavour there are.

What is the probability of pulling a meat flavour
bag out of the cupboard at random?

Write your answer in the simplest possible terms.

Flavour	Number
Smoky Bacon	10
Cheese and Onion	3
Roast Chicken	8
Ready Salted	1
Sweet Chilli	2

Method

1) Work out how many bags of crisps there are <u>in total</u>, and how many <u>meat flavour</u> bags there are.

> There are $10 + 3 + 8 + 1 + 2 = 24$ bags of crisps in total.
> There are 10 Smoky Bacon + 8 Roast Chicken = 18 meat flavour bags of crisps.

2) Write the number of meat flavour bags as a <u>fraction</u> of the total
number of bags and reduce it to its <u>lowest terms</u>.

3) The <u>probability</u> of picking a meat flavour bag is $\frac{3}{4}$.

> Probability $= \frac{18}{24} \quad \frac{3}{4}$
> $\div 6$
> $\div 6$

Q Players take it in turns to draw a line connecting two dots on this grid.
You 'win' a square if you draw the last side to complete a square.
The next line is drawn at random. Which point on the probability
scale shows the probability of winning a square on the next turn?

A   B   C   D   E

0   **Even**   1

Method

1) Count <u>how many places</u> you could draw a line, and how many of these will <u>complete a square</u>.

> There are 9 lines left to draw, and 3 of these will complete a square.

2) Work out the <u>probability</u> of completing a square, and see where it lies on the scale.

> The probability of completing a square $= \frac{3}{9} = \frac{1}{3}$.
>
> Point C is one third of the way along the scale, so C is the answer.

Practice Question

The numbers on the Venn diagram show the number of children in each section.

1) This Venn diagram represents a class of children.
A child is chosen at random. Which one of the following is true?

A There is an even chance that a boy or girl is selected.
B There is a one in four chance that the child selected wears glasses.
C There is a one-eighth chance that a boy glasses-wearer is selected.
D There is more chance of a glasses-wearer being selected than not.
E There is a 50% probability that a girl glasses-wearer is selected.

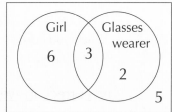

Section Four — Data Handling

Angles

The three main types of angle you need to learn are right angles, acute angles and obtuse angles.

Angles are Measured using Degrees (°)

Right angles measure exactly 90°.

Acute angles measure between 0 and 90°.

Obtuse angles measure between 90° and 180°.

Learn these Rules about Angles

Angles around a Point Add Up to 360°

The four angles total 360°.
So the missing angle is
360 − 51 − 72 − 158 = 79°.

Angles on a Straight Line Add Up to 180°

The two angles total 180°.
So the missing angle is
180 − 49 = 131°.

Angles in a Triangle Add Up to 180°

The three angles total 180°.
So the missing angle is
180 − 74 − 74 = 32°.

Angles in a Quadrilateral Add Up to 360°

The four angles total 360°.
So the missing angle is
360 − 84 − 79 − 56 = 141°.

11+ Style Questions

Q Estimate the size of angle x.

A 90°   **B** 30°   **C** 105°   **D** 75°   **E** 120°

Method

1) It's <u>smaller than 90°</u>, so it must be an <u>acute</u> angle.
That means option A is <u>incorrect</u> — it's a right angle.
Options C and E are also <u>incorrect</u> — they're <u>obtuse</u> angles.

You can't do a calculation here — you don't know the sizes of the other angles.

2) That leaves options B and D. You need to decide which option is <u>more realistic</u>.

If the angle was 30°, it would be three times smaller than a right angle.
When you compare angle x to a right angle, it's only a little bit smaller.
So, the angle must be 75° — it's the most realistic option.

You can compare an unknown angle with a right angle using the corner of a sheet of paper.

3) The <u>correct answer</u> is option <u>D</u> — 75°.

Q What is the size of the angle marked *a* between the two hands on this clock?

Method

1) The <u>total angle</u> around the centre point of the clock is <u>360°</u>.

2) There are <u>12 hours</u> equally spaced apart on the clock.
   Work out the size of the angle <u>between each hour</u>.

   Divide the total angle by the number of hours. → $360 \div 12 = 30°$ → The angle between each hour on the clock is 30°.

3) Work out <u>how many hours</u> apart the two hands are.

   The minute hand is at 12 and the hour hand is at 5. They are 5 hours apart.

4) <u>Multiply</u> the <u>number of hours</u> by <u>30°</u> to find the value of the missing angle.

   $5 \times 30 = 150°$. Angle *a* is 150°.

Q Ted made the following pattern using a rectangle and a triangle. What is the size of angle *x*?

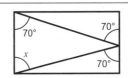

Method

1) Work out the <u>size</u> of the other angle in the triangle.

    Angles on a straight line add up to 180°.

   The angle is $180 - 70 - 70 = 40°$.

2) The three angles in a <u>triangle</u> add up to <u>180°</u>. Use this rule to work out the size of *x*:

    You have two angles of the triangle. Their total is $70 + 40 = 110°$.

   Angle *x* is the third angle in the triangle. It is $180 - 110 = 70°$.

Practice Questions

1) Estimate the size of angle *c*.
   A 100°   **B** 125°   **C** 10°   **D** 45°   **E** 90°

2) What is the size of the angle between the north east and south points on this compass?

Think about the total number of points on the compass.

Section Five — Shape and Space

2D Shapes

2D shapes are flat — they have length and width but no height.

Quadrilaterals are shapes with *Four Sides*

Make sure that you know the <u>properties</u> of these <u>quadrilaterals</u>.

Parallel lines have exactly the same slope.

Square

4 right angles

4 equal sides and 2 pairs of parallel sides

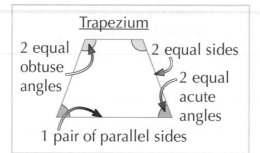

Trapezium

2 equal obtuse angles

2 equal sides

2 equal acute angles

1 pair of parallel sides

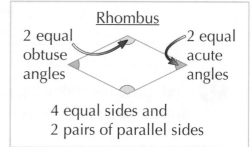

Rectangle

4 right angles

2 pairs of equal sides and 2 pairs of parallel sides

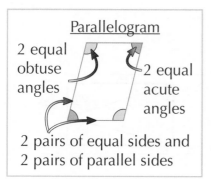

Parallelogram

2 equal obtuse angles

2 equal acute angles

2 pairs of equal sides and 2 pairs of parallel sides

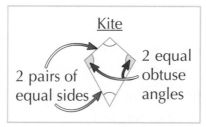

Kite

2 pairs of equal sides

2 equal obtuse angles

Rhombus

2 equal obtuse angles

2 equal acute angles

4 equal sides and 2 pairs of parallel sides

There are **Different Types** *of* **Triangle**

The angles in a triangle add up to 180° (see page 54).

1) *Equilateral* Triangle

3 equal angles — each angle measures 60°.

3 equal sides

2) *Isosceles* Triangle

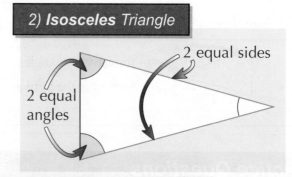

2 equal sides

2 equal angles

3) *Scalene* Triangle

No equal sides or angles

4) *Right-angled* Triangle

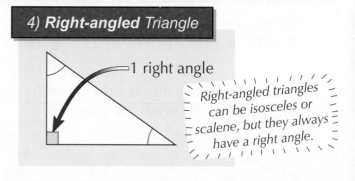

1 right angle

Right-angled triangles can be isosceles or scalene, but they always have a right angle.

Section Five — Shape and Space

Regular Polygons have Equal Sides and Angles

A polygon is a 2D shape with straight lines.

Regular Pentagon

5 equal sides and
5 equal angles

Regular Hexagon

6 equal sides and
6 equal angles

Regular Heptagon

7 equal sides and
7 equal angles

Regular Octagon

8 equal sides and
8 equal angles

Irregular polygons have at least one side or angle that's different in size. E.g. an irregular pentagon has five sides but at least one of the sides or angles is different to the others.

11+ Style Questions

Q Which of the following shapes should be placed in area Z of the Venn diagram?

A Square
B Rectangle
C Rhombus
D Isosceles Triangle
E Trapezium

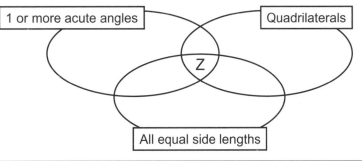

Method

1) Area Z is in the centre of the Venn diagram. You need to find the option that's a quadrilateral with 1 or more acute angles and all equal side lengths.

2) First, eliminate any options that aren't quadrilaterals.

   An isosceles triangle has 3 sides so it's not a quadrilateral. The answer isn't option D.

3) Next, eliminate the options that don't have all equal side lengths.

   Rectangles and trapeziums don't have all equal side lengths. The answer isn't option B or E.

4) That leaves A and C. Eliminate the option that doesn't have 1 or more acute angles.

   A square has 4 right angles. The answer isn't option A.

5) The correct answer must be a rhombus — option C.
   It's a quadrilateral with 2 acute angles and 4 equal sides.

Q Fran has a box containing identical trapezium tiles.
One of the tiles is shown. What is the size of angle *c*?

Method

1) Start by working out the size of the <u>other acute angle</u>.

A trapezium has two equal acute angles. So, this angle is also 82°.

There's more about acute angles and obtuse angles on page 54.

2) Work out the <u>total size</u> of the two <u>obtuse angles</u>.

A trapezium is a quadrilateral, so the total size of the angles is 360°.
This means that the total size of the two remaining angles is 360 – 82 – 82 = 196°.

3) You can now calculate the size of <u>angle *c*</u>.

A trapezium has two equal obtuse angles,
so the size of angle *c* is 196° ÷ 2 = 98°.

Q Tariq put five shapes into a bag. He pulled one out at random.
The shape had one pair of equal sides, no parallel sides and no obtuse angles.
Which of the following shapes did Tariq pull out of the bag?

A   B   C   D   E

Method

1) Work through <u>each option</u> until you find the one that <u>matches</u> the <u>description</u> of the shape.

Option A has one pair of parallel sides and two obtuse angles so it's incorrect.

Option B has five equal sides and five obtuse angles so it's incorrect.

Option C has two pairs of equal sides and two obtuse angles so it's incorrect.

Option D has one pair of equal sides, no parallel sides and no obtuse angles.

2) <u>Option D</u> matches the description of the shape that Tariq chose — this is the <u>correct</u> answer.
You <u>don't need</u> to look at <u>option E</u> now you know which one's correct.

Q Which shape should go in the grey box of the sorting table?

A Regular hexagon
B Equilateral triangle
C Regular pentagon
D Trapezium
E Rectangle

	At least one obtuse angle	No obtuse angles
All sides equal lengths		
One pair of equal length sides		

Method

1) First rule out the shapes that <u>don't fit</u> in the 'at least one obtuse angle' <u>column</u>.

> Equilateral triangles and rectangles don't have any obtuse angles so you can rule out B and E.

2) Then rule out the shapes that <u>don't fit</u> in the 'one pair of equal length sides' <u>row</u>.

> Regular hexagons and regular pentagons both have all equal length sides — you can rule out A and C.

3) So, the only shape that fits in the '<u>at least one obtuse angle</u>' column and the '<u>one pair of equal length sides</u>' row is a trapezium. The correct answer is <u>option D</u>.

Practice Questions

1) Rhona is describing a shape to her friends. She says that it has no right angles, no equal sides and no equal angles. What is the name of the shape that Rhona is describing?
   A Rectangle   B Isosceles triangle   C Scalene triangle   D Kite   E Trapezium

2) Which shape should go in the grey box of the sorting table?

A Trapezium
B Square
C Rectangle
D Equilateral triangle
E Rhombus

	All equal angles	Angles aren't all equal
All equal side lengths		
Side lengths aren't all equal		

3) Naomi is thinking of a shape. She gives David some clues about it:

- The shape has no obtuse angles.
- The shape has no right angles.
- Two of its sides are equal in length.

What shape is Naomi thinking of?

2D Shapes — Area and Perimeter

The length around the edge of a shape is its perimeter. The space covered by a shape is its area.

Warm-Up Activity

1) <u>Measure</u> one of the short and one of the long <u>edges</u> of a book cover using a <u>ruler</u>.
2) Use the measurements to try to work out the <u>perimeter</u> and <u>area</u> of the book cover.

Perimeter is the Length Around a Shape

1) To calculate the <u>perimeter</u> of a shape, <u>add up</u> the length of <u>every side</u> of the shape.

The shapes on this page aren't drawn to scale.

Add each side together:
11 + 5 + 11 + 5 = 32 cm → The perimeter of the rectangle is 32 cm.

Add each side together:
6 + 6 + 3 + 6 + 14.5 + 8 = 43.5 cm

2) Sometimes you <u>don't know</u> the length of every side. You need to <u>work out</u> the missing lengths.

You need to work out the length of this side.

The two shorter horizontal sides equal the length of the longer side opposite. So the missing side is 21 cm – 5 cm = 16 cm. Now add the sides together to find the perimeter: 21 + 6 + 16 + 6 + 5 + 12 = 66 cm.

This is a regular hexagon so all of the sides are equal. Add them together to find the perimeter: 4.5 + 4.5 + 4.5 + 4.5 + 4.5 + 4.5 = 27 cm (or 4.5 x 6 = 27 cm).

Area is the Space Inside a Shape

Finding the Area of a Square or Rectangle

<u>Multiply</u> the <u>length</u> by the <u>width</u> to work out the area of a square or rectangle.

The area of the rectangle = 7 × 12 = 84 cm²

Area is measured in square units, e.g. cm² and m².

Section Five — Shape and Space

Finding the **Area** of a **Triangle**

Calculate the area of a triangle by <u>multiplying</u> half of the
<u>base length</u> by the <u>height</u>.

half of the base length = 12 ÷ 2 = 6
half of the base length × height = 6 × 4 = 24 cm²

Finding the **Area** of **Other Shapes**

Sometimes you need to <u>split</u> a more complex shape into <u>smaller shapes</u> to calculate its area.

Split the shape into
two smaller rectangles
and calculate the area
of each one.

Area of rectangle 1
= 4 × 6 = 24 cm²

Area of rectangle 2
= 20 × 4 = 80 cm²

Add the area of the
two rectangles together
to find the total area:
24 + 80 = 104 cm²

11+ **Style** Questions

Q Yasmin used 5 identical rectangular tiles to make
the shape shown. The length of each tile is 16 cm
and the width of each tile is 8 cm.

What is the perimeter of the arrow shape
that's been made inside the grey tiles?

Method

1) Work out the <u>length</u> of each part of the shape.

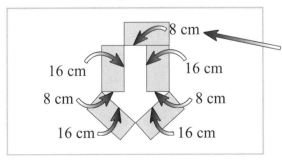

This side is the length of the top
rectangle minus the width of the
rectangle under it. 16 – 8 = 8 cm.

2) <u>Add</u> each side together to find the perimeter.

8 + 16 + 8 + 16 + 16 + 8 + 16 = 88 cm

Q Marcelo made this shape using one square and four identical isosceles triangles.

The total perimeter of the shape is 96 mm.

What is the length of line *a*?

Think about the length of the sides on an isosceles triangle.

Method

1) Look at the <u>lines</u> which make up the <u>perimeter</u> of Marcelo's shape.

> The perimeter of the shape is made using the two equal sides of four isosceles triangles.
> There are eight lines that make up the perimeter of the shape.
> The isosceles triangles are identical, so all eight lines must be the same length.

2) You know that the perimeter of the shape is 96 mm. So, <u>divide</u> the total perimeter by the number of lines to work out the length of <u>each line</u>.

> $96 \div 8 = 12$ mm

3) That gives you the answer — the length of line *a* is <u>12 mm</u>.

Q Mabel is building a new run for her rabbits. The run is made up of four rectangular fence panels which are each 200 cm in length and 40 cm in width. What is the total area of the fence panels that Mabel needs to make the run?

40 cm

200 cm

A 32 000 cm² **C** 40 000 cm² **E** 16 000 cm²

B 8000 cm² **D** 24 000 cm²

Method

1) Start by finding the area of <u>each rectangular panel</u>.

> The area of a rectangle = length × width
> So the area of each fence panel = 200 × 40 = 8000 cm²

You can easily do 200 × 40 — take off the three zeros and do 2 × 4 = 8, then add the three zeros back onto the answer — 8000.

2) <u>Multiply</u> this by the <u>number of panels</u> to find the <u>total area</u> of all of the fence panels.

> 8000 × 4 = 32 000 cm²

3) The total area of the fence panels used by Mabel is <u>32 000 cm²</u>. So the correct answer is <u>option A</u>.

Q The diagram shows the downstairs of Stephen's house. Stephen wants to lay a new carpet in his living room and his dining room. What is the area of carpet that Stephen needs?

A 35 m²   C 99 m²   E 51 m²

B 16 m²   D 63 m²

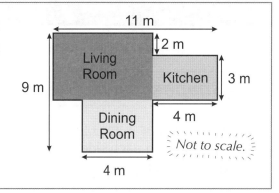

Method

1) You need to work out the areas of the living room and dining room <u>separately</u>, and then <u>add</u> them together.

2) Start by working out the <u>unknown lengths</u>.

The width of the living room is the width of the kitchen plus 2 metres.
3 + 2 = 5 m

The width of the dining room is the total width of the downstairs minus the width of the living room.
9 − 5 = 4 m

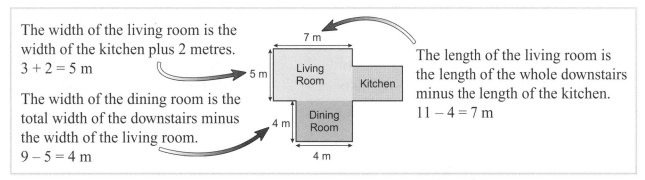

The length of the living room is the length of the whole downstairs minus the length of the kitchen.
11 − 4 = 7 m

3) Next, work out the area of the <u>living room</u> and the area of the <u>dining room</u>.

Area of the living room = 7 × 5 = 35 m²
Area of the dining room = 4 × 4 = 16 m²

4) <u>Add</u> the two areas together to find the <u>total area of carpet</u> that Stephen needs.

35 + 16 = 51 m² — option E is correct.

Practice Questions

1) This shape is made from two identical regular hexagons joined together.
The total perimeter of the shape is 75 cm.
How long is side *Z*?

2) Calculate the area of this shape.

A 48 cm²   C 64 cm²   E 96 cm²
B 72 cm²   D 132 cm²

Symmetry

Symmetrical shapes can be split into two identical halves. These halves are reflections of each other.

2D Shapes can be Symmetrical

line of symmetry

These two parts of the shape are reflections of each other.

1) If a shape has a <u>line of symmetry</u>, it means that both parts of the shape on each side of the line are <u>reflections</u> of <u>each other</u>.

2) Shapes can have <u>different numbers</u> of lines of symmetry (or no lines of symmetry). For example:

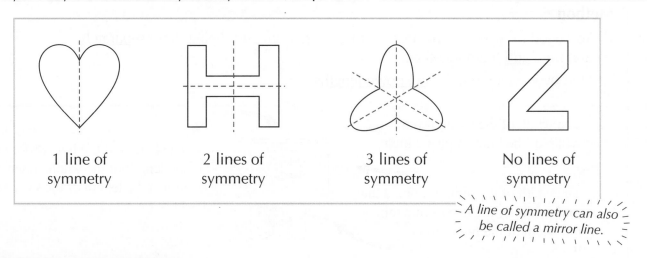

| 1 line of symmetry | 2 lines of symmetry | 3 lines of symmetry | No lines of symmetry |

A line of symmetry can also be called a mirror line.

11+ Style Questions

Q Charlene has drawn half of a shape. She reflects it in the mirror line to make a whole shape. What is the name of the whole shape?

mirror line

A Rhombus   **C** Pentagon   **E** Kite

B Parallelogram   **D** Hexagon

Method

1) You could sketch the shape and its <u>reflection</u> on some rough paper to show you what the <u>whole shape</u> will be.

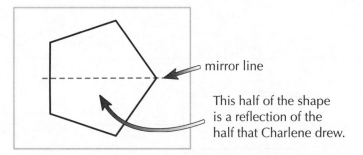

mirror line

This half of the shape is a reflection of the half that Charlene drew.

2) The whole shape has <u>five sides</u>. This means that it's a <u>pentagon</u> — <u>option C</u>.

Q How many lines of symmetry does this shape have?

Method

1) Start by looking for any <u>horizontal</u> or <u>vertical lines of symmetry</u>.

 These two halves of the shape are reflections of each other. So, there is a vertical line of symmetry here.

There is also a horizontal line of symmetry here.

2) Next, look for any <u>diagonal</u> lines of symmetry.

 There are two diagonal lines of symmetry here. The lines split the shape into two sets of identical halves.

3) The shape has <u>four lines of symmetry</u> in total.

 ## Tips and Tricks for Symmetry

If you're stuck in the exam, you can draw the shape on a scrap piece of paper and fold it in half. Unfold the paper again and look to see whether the two halves of the shape on either side of the fold line are symmetrical.

Practice Questions

1) What whole shape would you see when this half shape is reflected in the mirror line?

   A Trapezium   **C** Rhombus   **E** Hexagon
   B Parallelogram   **D** Pentagon

 mirror line

2) Elssie drew the following shape.
   How many lines of symmetry does it have?

3D Shapes

3D shapes are different from 2D shapes — they have length and width, but they also have height.

Learn *these common* **3D Shapes**

Cubes *and* Cuboids *have* Six Faces

Vertices are corners.

Cube
6 faces, 12 edges
and 8 vertices

Cuboid
6 faces, 12 edges
and 8 vertices

Pyramids *have* **Triangular Faces** *that join at a* **Point**

Triangle-based Pyramid
4 faces, 6 edges
and 4 vertices

Square-based Pyramid
5 faces, 8 edges
and 5 vertices

Prisms *have the* **Same Face** *at* **Each End**

Triangular Prism
5 faces, 9 edges
and 6 vertices

Pentagonal Prism
7 faces, 15 edges
and 10 vertices

Hexagonal Prism
8 faces, 18 edges
and 12 vertices

Nets *Fold* to make **3D Shapes**

1) 3D shapes can be made using a <u>net</u>. A net is a 2D shape which can be <u>folded</u> to make a 3D shape.

2) The shapes that make up the <u>net</u> become the faces of the <u>3D shape</u>.

3) There's often <u>more than one</u> net that you can use to make a 3D shape.

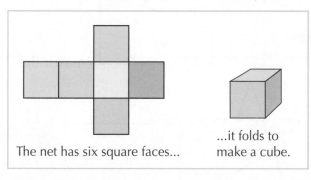

The net has six square faces...

...it folds to make a cube.

The net has four triangles around a square...

...it folds to make a square-based pyramid.

Volume of *Cubes* and *Cuboids* = *Length* × *Width* × *Height*

1) <u>Volume</u> is the amount of space <u>inside</u> a shape.
2) You can work out the volume of a cube or a cuboid by <u>multiplying</u> the <u>length</u>, <u>width</u> and <u>height</u> together.

Volume is measured in cubed units — e.g. m³ or cm³.

Length = 10 cm
Width = 5 cm
Height = 8 cm

$10 \times 5 \times 8 = 400 \text{ cm}^3$

11+ *Style* Questions

Q Sunita has made this net.
What shape will be made when the net is folded?

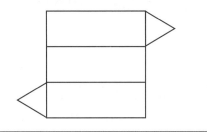

Method 1

<u>Imagine</u> the net being folded up. Work out <u>which edges</u> will <u>join</u> to <u>each other</u>.

These two edges will join together when the net is folded.

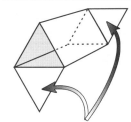

Fold in the triangular faces at each end of the shape.

The finished shape is a triangular prism.

Method 2

You could also work out the final shape by <u>looking</u> at the <u>number</u> of faces and the <u>shape</u> of the faces.

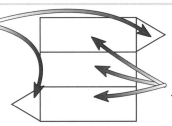

There are two identical triangular faces at each end of the shape.

There are three rectangular faces to join to the triangular ends. So, the finished shape will be a triangular prism.

Q Chloe's swimming pool is shown.
It can hold 48 m³ of water when full.
What is the height of the swimming pool?

A 1.5 m   C 12 m   E 8 m

B 4 m   D 2 m

4 m

?

6 m

Method

1) The <u>formula</u> to work out the volume of the pool is: <u>length × width × height</u>.

2) You know the volume, the length and the width, so you can use this to work out the <u>height</u>.

> length × width × height = 48 m³
> 6 × 4 × height = 48 m³
> 24 × height = 48 m³
> Now work out how many 24s make 48. 24 × 2 = 48.

You can check that your answer is correct by doing 6 × 4 × 2 = 48.

3) The height of the paddling pool is <u>2 m</u> — <u>option D</u>.

Q Oscar has a bag of identical dice of side 2 cm.
What is the maximum number of dice that he can fit in this box?

4 cm

10 cm

8 cm

Method

1) Start by working out <u>how many dice</u> fit along the <u>length</u> of the box.

> Each dice is 2 cm long and the box is 10 cm long. 10 ÷ 2 = 5 dice.

2) Next, work out <u>how many dice</u> fit along the <u>width</u> of the box.

> Each dice is 2 cm wide and the box is 8 cm wide. 8 ÷ 2 = 4 dice.

4 cm,
2 dice

10 cm, 5 dice

8 cm,
4 dice

3) Then, work out <u>how many dice</u> fit up the <u>height</u> of the box.

> Each dice is 2 cm high and the box is 4 cm high. 4 ÷ 2 = 2 dice.

4) To work out the <u>total number</u> of dice that will fit in the box, <u>multiply</u> the number of dice that fit in the <u>length</u>, by the number that fit in the <u>width</u>, and the number that fit up the <u>height</u>.

> 5 × 4 × 2 = 40. Oscar will be able to fit 40 dice in the box.

Q Joel folds this net to make a pentagonal prism.
Which corner is going to join to corner X?

Method

1) You need to imagine <u>how</u> the net will be folded to make the pentagonal prism.

2) Each corner of the <u>two pentagons</u> will join with a corner of a <u>rectangle</u>.

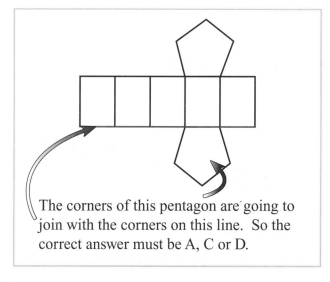

The corners of this pentagon are going to join with the corners on this line. So the correct answer must be A, C or D.

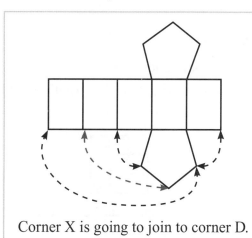

Corner X is going to join to corner D. So, the correct answer is option D.

Practice Questions

1) Which of these nets will not fold to make a cube?

   A   **B**   **C**   **D**   **E**

2) Vegetable stock cubes have sides that are 1 cm long. How many vegetable stock cubes will fit in a box that is 4 cm long, 8 cm wide and 2 cm high?

3) Frankie has made this net.
What shape will be made when the net is folded?

Section Five — Shape and Space

Shape Problems

Some questions will ask you to picture in your head what shapes will look like when they're flipped, rotated or moved around. Here are some sample questions to help you get the idea.

Q Lily has two blocks made out of square tiles. She fits them together to make some new shapes. She does not overlap the two blocks. Which of the following shapes can Lily not make?

A   B   C   D   E

Method

1) Look at <u>each</u> answer option and see if it can be made from Lily's blocks.

2) You need to imagine <u>rotating the blocks</u> to see if they can make the shapes.

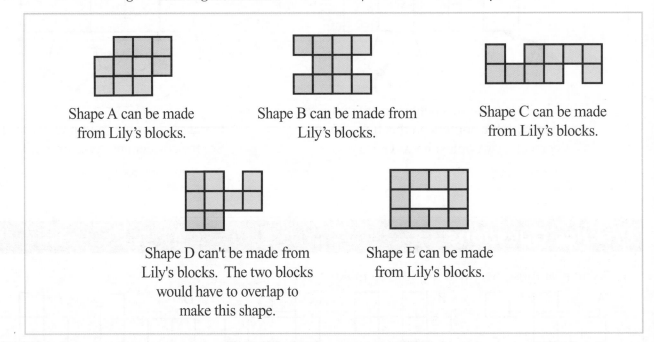

Shape A can be made from Lily's blocks.

Shape B can be made from Lily's blocks.

Shape C can be made from Lily's blocks.

Shape D can't be made from Lily's blocks. The two blocks would have to overlap to make this shape.

Shape E can be made from Lily's blocks.

3) <u>Option D</u> is the correct answer — it can't be made from the blocks used by Lily.

Tips and Tricks for Shape Problems

If you're stuck with a question like this in the exam, you could sketch the options on a rough piece of paper. Then try to shade in the two blocks to see if both of them fit into the shape.

Q Which of the following options shows this 3D shape when it has been rotated?

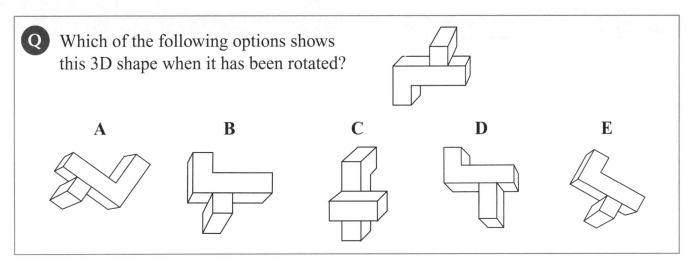

A   B   C   D   E

Method

1) You need to <u>imagine</u> the original 3D shape being <u>rotated</u>.

2) Start by <u>rotating the shape</u> in one direction.

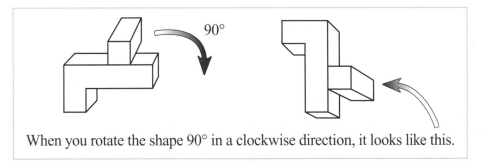

When you rotate the shape 90° in a clockwise direction, it looks like this.

3) The shape <u>doesn't match</u> any of the answer options. So try rotating it in a <u>different direction</u>.

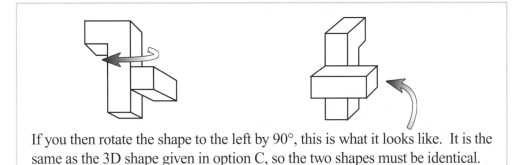

If you then rotate the shape to the left by 90°, this is what it looks like. It is the same as the 3D shape given in option C, so the two shapes must be identical.

4) That gives you the answer. The correct answer is <u>option C</u>.

Practice Question

1) The diagram shows how a logo on a window appears when viewed from the front. Which of the following options shows the same logo when viewed from the back?

A   B   C   D   E

Coordinates

Coordinates are pairs of numbers that help you to find points on a grid.

Compass Points *tell you about* Direction

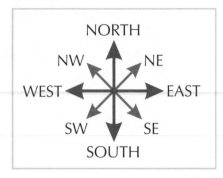

1) The <u>four</u> main compass directions are <u>north</u>, <u>south</u>, <u>east</u> and <u>west</u>.

2) The directions <u>halfway between</u> the four main directions are <u>north east</u>, <u>south east</u>, <u>south west</u> and <u>north west</u>.

Coordinates *show a* Point *on a* Grid

1) Each point on a grid has <u>two numbers</u> to show its position. These are <u>coordinates</u>.

2) The first number shows the position on the <u>horizontal *x*-axis</u>.
   The second number shows the position on the <u>vertical *y*-axis</u>.

3) Coordinates are always written <u>in brackets</u>, for example (0, 0) or (5, 4).

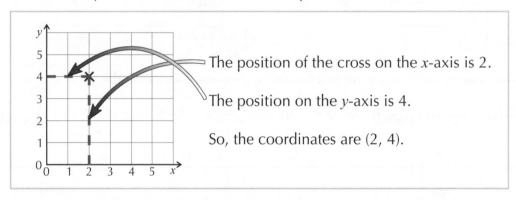

The position of the cross on the *x*-axis is 2.

The position on the *y*-axis is 4.

So, the coordinates are (2, 4).

Shapes *can be* Transformed *on a* Coordinate Grid

Reflection *in a* Line

1) Shapes can be <u>reflected</u> across a <u>mirror line</u> on a coordinate grid.

2) Each point and its reflection are exactly the <u>same distance</u> from the mirror line.

This is the reflection of the shape.

This point on the original shape is one square away from the mirror line. So, the same point on the reflected shape is also one square away from the mirror line.

Section Five — Shape and Space

Translation is Sliding a Shape

<u>Translation</u> is when a shape is <u>moved</u> from one place to another, without being flipped or rotated.

This shape has been translated by moving it 5 squares right and 4 squares down:

When you translate a shape, the new shape should look exactly the same as the original.

For the red point (4, 9), the *x*-coordinate on the translated shape will be 5 greater, and the *y*-coordinate will be 4 fewer.

The *x*-coordinate of this corner will be 4 + 5 = 9 and the *y*-coordinate will be 9 − 4 = 5 — (9, 5).

Rotation about a Point

The <u>point</u> you rotate a shape around is called the <u>centre of rotation</u>.

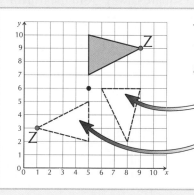

This shape has been rotated 180° clockwise using (5, 6) as the centre of rotation:

Rotate the shape 90°...

... and then another 90°.

11+ Style Questions

Q A rectangle was drawn on a coordinate grid. What are the coordinates of corner A?

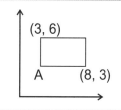

Method

1) You can use the coordinates you've been given to work out the coordinates of <u>corner A</u>.

These two corners are on the same position on the *x*-axis. The *x*-axis coordinate of the top corner is 3, so the *x*-axis coordinate of A is also 3.

These two corners are on the same position on the *y*-axis. The *y*-axis coordinate of the right-hand corner is 3, so the *y*-axis coordinate of A is also 3.

2) That gives you the <u>*x*-axis</u> and <u>*y*-axis</u> coordinates. So, the coordinates of corner A are (<u>3, 3</u>).

Q Gurbaj drew this shape on a coordinate grid. What are the coordinates of point X when Gurbaj reflects the shape in the mirror line?

Method

Point X on the <u>reflected shape</u> will be the <u>same distance</u> from the mirror line as point X on the original shape.

If you're allowed to write on the exam paper, you could draw the reflection of the shape.

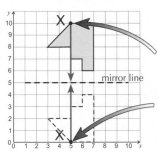

The shape has been reflected vertically, so the x-coordinate is still the same (5).

The y-coordinate of point X is 10, and the y-coordinate of the mirror line is 5. So, point X is $10 - 5 = 5$ squares away from the mirror line.

The reflected point X will also be 5 squares away from the mirror line. So, the y-coordinate will be $5 - 5 = 0$.

The coordinates of the reflected point X are $(5, 0)$.

Q Abi is walking from her house at point Z to her school at point W. Which of the following describes her route?

A 3 squares north, 4 squares east, 1 square north

B 2 squares east, 4 squares north, 2 squares east

C 6 squares north, 3 squares east, 1 square south

D 1 square south, 5 squares east, 5 squares north

E 4 squares east, 2 squares north, 3 squares west

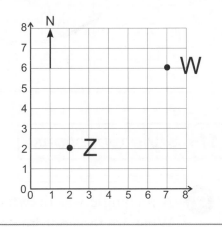

Method

1) Starting at point Z, <u>follow</u> each route on the grid.

2) Remember, you're looking for the route that <u>finishes at point W</u>.

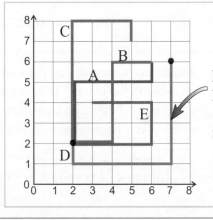

D is the only route that will lead Abi to her school.

So, option D is the correct answer.

Q Yohan draws a square on a grid. The coordinates of the four corners are (3, 5), (7, 5), (3, 9) and (7, 9). Which of the following points is inside Yohan's square?

    A (7, 3)   **B** (6, 4)   **C** (9, 8)   **D** (6, 8)   **E** (5, 4)

Method

1) You can use the <u>coordinates</u> that you've been <u>given</u> to work out which of the coordinates is <u>within</u> the square.

> The x-coordinates of the corners of the square are 3, 7, 3 and 7.
> So to be inside the square, the point must have an x-coordinate between 3 and 7.

> The y-coordinates of the corners of the square are 5, 5, 9 and 9.
> So to be inside the square, the point must have a y-coordinate between 5 and 9.

> In option D, the x-coordinate (6) is between 3 and 7, and the y-coordinate (8) is between 5 and 9. So the point (6, 8) is inside Yohan's square.

2) That gives you the answer — <u>option D</u> is the only option that's <u>inside</u> the square.

Practice Questions

1) Nadine is plotting a parallelogram on this coordinate grid.
She plots two of the corners at (1, 3) and (2, 6).
Which of the following could be the coordinates of the other two corners?

  A (4, 3) and (5, 4)   **C** (6, 5) and (6, 4)   **E** (3, 2) and (4, 7)
  B (5, 5) and (7, 7)   **D** (7, 6) and (6, 3)

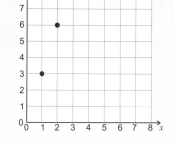

2) What will the coordinates of corner Y be after this triangle has been rotated 90° anticlockwise about the point (6, 7)?

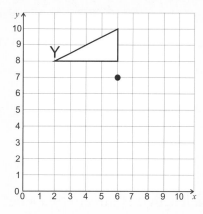

Section Five — Shape and Space

Units

For the exam, you'll need to be able to convert between different size units of measurement, as well as have an idea of how big each one is.

Warm-Up Activity

Have a look at some tins, packets and bottles from your kitchen cupboards. Try to guess the <u>mass</u> or <u>volume</u> of each. Check the labels to see how close you were.

There are Units for **Length**, **Mass** and **Volume**

1) Here's a bit about the different <u>units of length</u>:

Your finger is about 1 cm wide.

A flea is about 2 mm long.

A door is about 2 m tall.

1 centimetre = 10 millimetres
1 metre = 100 centimetres
1 kilometre = 1000 metres

10 football pitches laid end-to-end would be about 1 km.

2) Here's a bit about the different <u>units of mass</u>:

A paper clip has a mass of about 1 g.

A bag of sugar usually has a mass of 1 kg.

1 kilogram = 1000 grams

'Capacity' is the volume that something can hold when it's full, e.g. the capacity of a carton of juice is 1 l.

3) Here's a bit about the different <u>units of volume</u>:

A bottle of squash can hold about 1 l.

1 litre = 1000 millilitres

A small drop of water is about 1 ml.

Convert between **Large** and **Small** Units by **Multiplying** or **Dividing**

1) You might need to <u>convert</u> a <u>smaller</u> unit into a <u>larger</u> unit or a <u>larger</u> unit into a <u>smaller</u> one.

2) To convert a larger unit to a smaller unit you need to <u>multiply</u>. For example:

To convert a mass that's in kg to a mass that's in g, multiply by 1000 (because there are 1000 g in a kg).　　3.6 kg ⟹ 3.6 × 1000 = 3600 g

3) To convert a smaller unit to a larger unit you need to <u>divide</u>. For example:

To convert a length that's in cm to a length that's in m, divide by 100 (because there are 100 cm in a m).　　40 cm ⟹ 40 ÷ 100 = 0.4 m

11+ Style *Questions*

> **Q** Which of the following statements is true?
>
> A   There are 100,000 millilitres in 10 litres
> B   There are 100,000 grams in 10 kilograms
> C   There are 100,000 millimetres in 1 kilometre
> D   There are 100,000 centimetres in 1 kilometre
> E   There are 100,000 millimetres in 0.1 metres

Method

1) Take each statement in turn and check whether it's <u>true</u>.

> A   1 litre = 1000 ml, so 10 litres = 10 × 1000 ml = 10 000 ml — false.
> B   1 kg = 1000 g, so 10 kg = 10 × 1000 g = 10 000 g — false.
> C   1 km = 1000 m, 1 m = 100 cm and 1 cm = 10 mm, so 1 km = 1000 × 100 × 10 mm
>   = 1 000 000 mm — false.
> D   1 km = 1000 m and 1 m = 100 cm, so 1 km = 1000 × 100 cm = 100 000 cm — true.
> So the answer is D.

2) If you have time, <u>check your answer</u> by making sure E is false.

> E   0.1 m = 10 cm and 1 cm = 10 mm, so 0.1 m = 10 × 10 mm = 100 mm,
>   so statement E is also false.

> **Q** This glass holds 0.5 litres when it is full.
> Which of the following is most likely to be the volume of water in it?
>
> A 15 ml   B 165 ml   C 330 ml   D 33 ml   E 500 ml

Method

1) Work out how many <u>millilitres</u> of water there would be in a <u>full glass</u>.

> 1 litre = 1000 ml, so in 0.5 litres there will be 1000 ml ÷ 2 = 500 ml.

2) Estimate the <u>fraction</u> of the glass that is filled.

> It's about one third full. So the volume of water in the glass will be about one third of 500 ml.
> 500 ml ÷ 3 is a hard calculation, so estimate using an easier calculation — 600 ml ÷ 3 = 200 ml.
> 600 ml is larger than 500 ml, so you'd expect the answer to be a bit smaller than 200 ml.

3) Check which of the choices <u>match</u> your estimate.

> There's only one that's close — 165 ml, so the answer must be B.

Section Six — Units and Measures

Q Jo has 1.6 kg of hot chocolate powder. She puts 30 g of powder in each of 5 mugs of hot water. How much hot chocolate powder does Jo have left?

A 1.57 kg   B 1.3 kg   C 1.45 kg   D 0.1 kg   E 1.585 kg

Method

1) First work out how many grams of hot chocolate have been <u>used</u>.

> 30 g in each of 5 mugs is a total of 30 × 5 = 150 g.

2) To find out how much hot chocolate is left you need to <u>subtract 150 g from 1.6 kg</u>, so make the <u>units</u> the <u>same</u>. The answers are in <u>kg</u>, so make the units <u>both kg</u>.

> 150 g ÷ 1000 = 0.15 kg

3) Now <u>subtract</u> to find the mass of chocolate powder left.

> 1.6 kg – 0.15 kg = 1.45 kg. So the answer is C.

Q A stalactite is hanging from a cave ceiling. It is currently 22 cm long. If it grows at a rate of 0.2 mm per year, how long, in centimetres, will it be in 200 years' time?

Method

1) First, find out how much the stalactite will <u>grow in 200 years</u> by multiplying 0.2 mm by 200.

> The quick way to do 0.2 × 200 is to work out 0.2 × 100, and multiply the result by 2.
> 0.2 × 100 = 20. 20 × 2 = 40 mm.

2) You need to add the new growth to the stalactite's <u>current length</u> — but first make sure the <u>units</u> are the <u>same</u>.

> As you want the final answer in cm, convert the new growth to cm.
> 1 cm = 10 mm, so divide 40 mm by 10 to get the number of cm. 40 ÷ 10 = 4 cm.

3) Now <u>add</u> the current length and the new growth to find the length in 200 years' time.

> Length of stalactite = 22 cm + 4 cm = 26 cm

Practice Questions

1) Which of the following is most likely to be the mass of Tim's schoolbag with all of his books in?
   A 0.3 g   B 3 g   C 30 g   D 3 kg   E 30 kg

2) There are 28.75 litres of soup. 350 ml is spilt, and the rest is divided into 400 ml servings. How many servings are there?

3) Ben's stride is 50 cm. How many strides must he take to walk 10 km?
   A 20 000   B 2000   C 200 000   D 500   E 5000

Section Six — Units and Measures

Time

There's a lot to remember for this topic. Time to get prepared...

There are lots of **Different Units** for **Measuring Time**

1) Here's how some of the different <u>units of time</u> are <u>related</u> to each other.

> 1 minute = 60 seconds
> 1 hour = 60 minutes
> 1 day = 24 hours
> 1 year = 365 days (366 in a leap year)

Leap years occur every 4 years. The extra day is added to February.

2) There are <u>7 days</u> in a week and <u>52 weeks</u> in a <u>year</u>.

3) Months are a bit more tricky — there are <u>12 months</u> in a year, but the number of days in each month is <u>different</u>.

4) You can memorise the number of <u>days</u> in <u>each month</u> using this poem.

> "30 days has September, April, June and November.
> All the rest have 31, except February alone,
> Which has 28 days clear, and 29 in each leap year."

Don't Get Confused between **Morning** and **Evening**

1) The <u>hours</u> on a <u>12-hour clock</u> are shown by the numbers <u>1-12</u>. The numbers then have either "<u>am</u>" or "<u>pm</u>" after them to show you whether it's <u>morning</u> or <u>evening</u>.

2) "<u>am</u>" runs from 12 midnight to 11.59 in the morning.

3) "<u>pm</u>" runs from 12 noon to 11.59 at night.

4) 24-hour time is the <u>same</u> as 12-hour time if it's <u>morning</u>, e.g. 9:00 am is the same as 09:00 on a 24-hour clock.

5) But you have to <u>add on 12 hours</u> if it's <u>afternoon</u> or <u>evening</u>, e.g. 1.00 pm is the same as 13.00 on a 24-hour clock.

24-hour times always have 4 digits. A "0" is added to the front if it's before 10:00.

6) When it gets to <u>midnight</u>, the 24-hour clock goes from 23:59 to <u>00:00</u>.

11+ **Style** Questions

Q Which of the following 24-hour times is the same as ten to three in the afternoon?
A 15:10 B 02:50 C 15:50 D 14:50 E 03:50

Method

1) "Ten to three" in the afternoon in 12-hour time is <u>2:50 pm</u>.

2) Because it's in the <u>afternoon</u>, you add 12 hours to convert it to the 24-hour clock.

> 2:50 + 12 hours = 14:50. So the answer is D.

Q John spent 45 minutes weeding and then 52 minutes mowing the grass. How long did he spend gardening?

A 1.37 hours   B 1 hour 37 minutes   C 137 hours   D 9.7 hours   E 97 hours

Method

1) Add the number of minutes together to get the <u>total</u>. ⟹ $45 + 52 = 97$ minutes

2) Convert this to <u>hours and minutes</u>.

> There are 60 minutes in one hour. If you subtract 60 from 97 you're left with 37 minutes
> $(97 - 60 = 37)$. So 97 minutes = 1 hour and 37 minutes — the answer is B.

1.37 hours is not the same as 1 hour 37 minutes because there are 60 minutes in 1 hour and not 100.

Q Jane was born on Saturday 8th March. What day of the week was Ben born on if he was born on 4th May the same year?

Method

1) First, find <u>how many days</u> there are <u>between</u> the two dates. You can do this in short, easy stages — write down the numbers of days in <u>each month</u> between the dates.

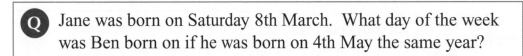

8th March $31 - 8 = \underline{23}$ days   31st March   <u>30</u> days   30th April   <u>4</u> days   4th May

Now add up the number of days: $23 + 30 + 4 = 57$ days

2) There are 7 days in a week, so every <u>7th</u> day after 8th March will be a Saturday too. Find the <u>multiple of 7</u> which is closest to 57.

> $8 \times 7 = 56$. So the 56th day after 8th March is a Saturday.

3) Now work out the <u>day</u> that 4th May falls on.

> There are 57 days between 8th March and 4th May, and the 56th day is a Saturday.
> So 4th May must be a Sunday.

Tips and Tricks for Time Questions

The method used to find the difference between two dates can be used to find the difference between two times. E.g. to find the number of minutes between 9:46 am and 11:31 am:

9:46   14 mins   10:00   60 mins   11:00   31 mins   11:31

$14 + 60 + 31 = 105$ minutes

Q Hannah needs to get to Millham by 2 pm. What is the latest that she can get a bus from Dale Street?

Ulverstown	1254	1314	1334	1404
Dale Street	1259	1319	1339	1409
Railway Station	1308	1327	1348	1417
Canal Foot		1340		1430
Millham	1324	1347	1404	1437
Daltown	1345	1411	1425	1511

Times in timetables are often written without a colon, so 1254 is the same as 12:54.

Method

1) Hannah needs to get to Millham by <u>2 pm</u>, but the timetable is in <u>24-hour clock time</u>. Convert 2 pm to the 24-hour clock.

   It's in the afternoon, so add 12 hours: 2 pm = 2 + 12 = 14:00

2) Now find the row for <u>Millham</u>.
   This lists the times that buses arrive there.

3) Find the <u>latest time</u> before 14:00 that Hannah can arrive at Millham.

   The bus that arrives at 14:04 is too late.
   The one before gets in at 13:47.

Ulverstown	1254	1314	1334	1404
Dale Street	1259	1319	1339	1409
Railway Station	1308	1327	1348	1417
Canal Foot		1340		1430
Millham	1324	1347	1404	1437
Daltown	1345	1411	1425	1511

4) Look <u>up the column</u> to find when this bus leaves Dale Street.

   It leaves Dale Street at 13:19.

Practice Questions

1) Some children's birthdays are given below. Which child is youngest?

   Meg — 14th May 2009   Fred — 16th March 2009   Geeta — 1st February 2008
   Jim — 28th December 2008   Max — 13th October 2009

2) Kerry completes one page of her Maths book each day, starting on 1st September.
   If there are 154 pages, in which month will she finish her book?

3) Jamie starts his homework at 4.53 pm. If he finishes it at 7.15 pm, how long did it take?

   A 2.22 hours   **C** 22 hours 2 minutes   **E** 3 hours 38 minutes
   B 202 minutes   **D** 2 hours 22 minutes

Mixed Problems

Some questions test your knowledge of more than one topic, so you might have to read a pie chart and work out some angles. The questions on these pages are examples, but you could be tested on any different combination of topics.

Warm-Up Activity

<u>Draw</u> a <u>line</u> between the calculations which have the <u>same answer</u>.

10% of 40	30 + 26
$5^2 - 10$	54 + 19
$(5 + 3) \times 7$	¼ of 16
0.73×100	3×5

11+ Style Questions

 A cruise ship travels $30\frac{1}{2}$ kilometres every hour.
It left port at 7 pm on Monday and arrived at its destination at 1 am on Tuesday.

How far did it travel?

Method

1) Work out how many <u>hours</u> the cruise ship was <u>travelling</u> for.

> On Monday the ship travelled for 5 hours between 7 pm and 12 am.
> On Tuesday the ship travelled for 1 hour between 12 am and 1 am.
> 5 + 1 = 6 hours.

2) Now multiply <u>6 hours</u> by <u>30 $\frac{1}{2}$ kilometres</u>.

> Use partitioning to find $6 \times 30\frac{1}{2}$. Partition $30\frac{1}{2}$ into 30 and $\frac{1}{2}$.
> $6 \times 30 = 180$, and $6 \times \frac{1}{2} = 3$ (it's the same as half of 6).
> Add together your results, 180 + 3 = 183 km.

3) The ship travelled <u>183 kilometres</u>.

Q Dylan has some shapes
which have areas *q* and *r*.

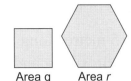

Area q   Area r

He cuts some of his shapes
in half and makes a pattern.

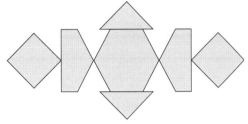

What is the area of the pattern?
A 2*q* + 3*r*   C 3*q* + 2*r*   E 4*q* + 4*r*
B 3*q* + *r*   D 3*q* + 4*r*

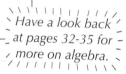

*Have a look back
at pages 32-35 for
more on algebra.*

Method

1) Work out what shapes make up the <u>pattern</u>.

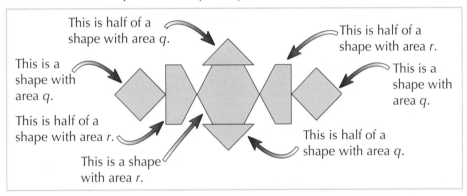

This is half of a
shape with area *q*.

This is half of a
shape with area *r*.

This is a
shape with
area *q*.

This is a
shape with
area *q*.

This is half of a
shape with area *r*.

This is half of a
shape with area *q*.

This is a shape
with area *r*.

2) Now <u>add together</u> all of the <u>areas</u>.

> There are two whole shapes and two half shapes with area *q*: $2 + \frac{1}{2} + \frac{1}{2} = 3$.
> The pattern has a total of 3 shapes with area *q*, so these shapes have an area of 3*q*.
>
> There is one whole shape and two half shapes with area *r*: $1 + \frac{1}{2} + \frac{1}{2} = 2$.
> The pattern has a total of 2 shapes with area *r*, so these shapes have an area of 2*r*.
>
> The total area of the pattern is the areas of the shapes added together, 3*q* + 2*r*.

3) So the <u>answer</u> is <u>C</u>.

Tips and Tricks for Mixed Problems

Make sure you read mixed problem questions very carefully.

They can look quite difficult, but you just need to take your time

and work out what steps you need to follow to find the answer.

Q Cliff wants to varnish all four walls of his barn.

Two of the walls of the barn are 15 metres long and 2.5 metres high. The other two walls are 9 metres long and 2.5 metres high.

1 litre of varnish will cover 10 square metres.

How many litres of varnish does he need?

Method

1) Work out the <u>total area</u> of all of the <u>walls</u>.

> The area of a rectangle = length × height.
> The lengths of all the walls would be 15 + 15 + 9 + 9 = 48 m.
> So the area of all the walls = 48 m × 2.5 m.
>
> Use partitioning to find 48 × 2.5. Partition 2.5 into 2 and 0.5.
> 48 × 2 = 96, and 48 × 0.5 = 24 (it's the same as half of 48).
> Add together your results, 96 + 24 = 120 m².

You could also work out the area of each wall and add them together.

2) Work out how many <u>litres</u> of <u>varnish</u> are needed to <u>cover</u> the <u>four walls</u>.

> 1 litre of varnish will cover 10 m². So 120 ÷ 10 = 12.
> 12 litres of varnish will cover the walls of the barn.

 Q Calculate the size of angle x.
A 25°   D 15°
B 40°   E 10°
C 30°

Method

1) Use the information you have to make an <u>equation</u>.

> Angles in a triangle add up to 180°.
> One of the angles is a right angle (90°) so the other
> two angles must add up to 180° − 90° = 90°.
> $2x + x = 90°$
> So $3x = 90°$.

2) Use your <u>equation</u> to find the size of <u>angle x</u>.

> Find x when $3x = 90°$.
> $3x = 90°$ The opposite of × 3 is ÷ 3,
> ÷ 3   ÷ 3   so divide both sides by 3.
>
> $x = 30°$ That gives you the answer — x is 30°.
>   C is correct.

Q Jason's class conducted a survey. They asked the teachers who drove to school how many passengers they took with them.

They collected their results in a bar chart.

What percentage of the teachers travelled with 3 passengers?

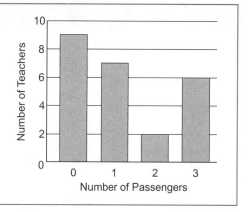

Method

1) First work out <u>how many teachers</u> took part in the <u>survey</u>.

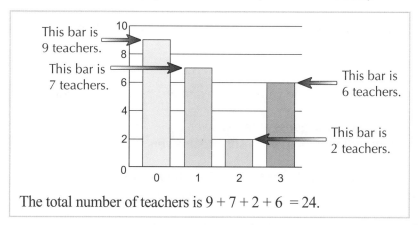

This bar is 9 teachers.

This bar is 7 teachers.

This bar is 6 teachers.

This bar is 2 teachers.

The total number of teachers is $9 + 7 + 2 + 6 = 24$.

2) Now you can work out the <u>percentage</u> of <u>teachers</u> who travelled with <u>3 passengers</u>.

6 teachers out of a total of 24 travelled with three passengers. This gives you the fraction $\frac{6}{24}$. This fraction can be simplified to $\frac{1}{4}$.

$$\frac{6}{24} = \frac{1}{4} \longrightarrow \frac{1}{4} = 25\%$$

3) The <u>percentage</u> of <u>teachers</u> who travelled with <u>3 passengers</u> is <u>25%</u>.

Practice Questions

1) A swimming pool is 10 metres long, 10 metres wide and 1.6 metres deep.
   It costs 25p to fill 1 m³ of the pool with water.
   What is the cost of filling the pool to the top?

2) Mr O'Brian recorded the colour of the flowers in his garden in a pie chart. What percentage of his flowers were red?

   A 5%
   B 12.5%
   C 25%
   D 42%
   E 54%

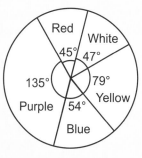

Section Seven — Mixed Problems

Glossary

acute angles	Angles that measure <u>less than</u> 90°. They are <u>smaller</u> than <u>right angles</u>.
area	The <u>amount of space</u> covered by a 2D (flat) shape. It is measured in <u>square units</u> (e.g. cm²).
average	A <u>typical</u> (or 'normal' value). There are three kinds of average — <u>mean</u>, <u>median</u> and <u>mode</u>.
coordinates	They tell you the <u>position</u> of a point on a grid. For example, (3, 4) means 3 units along the <u>horizontal *x*-axis</u> and 4 units up the <u>vertical *y*-axis</u>.
decimal places	The <u>places in a number</u> to the <u>right</u> of the decimal point. For example, the number 4.56 has 2 decimal places.
degrees, °	The units used to measure <u>angles</u>. For example, a right angle measures 90°.
denominator	The <u>bottom number</u> of a fraction.
equivalent	Something that has the same value. For example, ½ and ²⁄₄ are <u>equivalent fractions</u>.
estimate	An estimate is a <u>sensible guess</u> at the answer. You can use <u>rounding</u> to help you estimate answers.
factor	A whole number that divides exactly into another whole number. For example, the factors of 6 are 1, 2, 3 and 6.
frequency	<u>How many times</u> something appears in a set of data.
mass	Mass is what most people mean when they say 'weight'. A <u>brick</u> has a greater mass than a loaf of <u>bread</u>. Mass is measured in grams or kilograms.
multiple	Multiples are the <u>numbers</u> in a <u>times table</u> that goes on forever. For example, the multiples of 4 are 4, 8, 12, 16....
numerator	The <u>top number</u> of a fraction.
obtuse angles	Angles that measure <u>more than</u> 90° but less than 180°. They're <u>bigger</u> than <u>right angles</u>.
parallel	Parallel lines, faces and edges are always the <u>same distance apart</u>. They will <u>never meet</u> or <u>cross</u>.
perimeter	The distance around the <u>outside</u> of a shape.
perpendicular	Lines, faces or edges that meet each other at <u>right angles</u> (or would meet at right angles if you extended them) are perpendicular.
polygon	A <u>2D</u> (flat) shape with <u>straight sides</u>.
prime	A <u>prime number</u> is a number that has exactly <u>two</u> factors: <u>1 and itself</u>. For example, 2, 3, 5 and 7 are all prime numbers.
square number	The result of <u>multiplying</u> a number by <u>itself</u>. For example, 2 × 2 = 4, 3 × 3 = 9. 4 and 9 are both square numbers.

Answers

SECTION ONE — NUMBER KNOWLEDGE

PAGES 4-5 — PLACE VALUE

Warm-Up Activity
10 000 — Biggest, 1 — Smallest
The numbers in order from smallest to biggest are 1, 10, 100, 1000, 10 000. 10 000 is the biggest and 1 is the smallest.

1. E
All the numbers have the same units, 8, so you need to look at the tenths. 4 of the numbers have 4 in the tenths (Option B has 5, so it's not the answer), which means you need to look at the hundredths. Option E has the smallest number of hundredths, 3, so E is the answer.

2. B
A — incorrect, the numbers are 0.03 and 0.3 away from 7.
B — correct, both numbers are 0.11 away from 7.
C — incorrect, the numbers are 0.2 and 0.02 away from 7.
D — incorrect, the numbers are 0.06 and 0.1 away from 7.
E — incorrect, the numbers are 0.1 and 0.19 away from 7.

PAGE 7 — ROUNDING UP AND DOWN

1. D
In 174 782, the 7 (in the ten thousands column) is being rounded. The 4 (in the thousands column) is less than 5 so 174 782 rounds down to 170 000.

PAGE 11 — NUMBER KNOWLEDGE

1. E
A — false, 3 is a factor of 24 and is not a multiple of 2.
B — false, 13 is a common factor of 13 and 52.
C — false, not all numbers ending in 3 are multiples of 3, e.g. 13.
D — false, no prime number is a square number. A prime number only has 2 factors, one and itself.
E — true, 3 is a prime number and a multiple of 3.

2. C
72 can be divided exactly by 4, 6, 8 and 9.
$72 \div 4 = 18$, $72 \div 6 = 12$, $72 \div 8 = 9$, $72 \div 9 = 8$.
But, 72 doesn't divide exactly by 7.

PAGES 12-13 — NUMBER SEQUENCES

Warm-Up Activity
9 and 47
The difference between each number in the sequence is 9 (e.g. $2 + 9 = 11$). The next number in the sequence is $38 + 9 = 47$.

1. 39
The sequence is 4, 9, 15. The difference between the numbers is increased by one each time. So the difference between 4 and 9 is 5, and 9 and 15 is 6. To find the fourth number you'd add 7, to find the fifth you'd add 8, and to find the sixth you'd add 9.
$15 + 7 = 22$. $22 + 8 = 30$. $30 + 9 = 39$.

PAGE 16 — FRACTIONS

1. E
Lydia gave Gemma $\frac{2}{5}$ of her pie. So Lydia is left with $\frac{3}{5}$ of a pie. Rose gave Gemma $\frac{1}{5}$ of her pie. So Rose is left with $\frac{4}{5}$ and Gemma has $\frac{2}{5} + \frac{1}{5} = \frac{3}{5}$ of a pie. So Lydia and Gemma have the same amount of pie.

2. B
Ilya and Alex share two bags of 6 apples, so the total number of apples = 12. To find the number taken by each person you could divide 12 by the denominator and then multiply the result by the numerator.
Ilya took $\frac{1}{4}$ of 12 apples: $12 \div 4 = 3$, $3 \times 1 = 3$ apples.
Alex took $\frac{2}{3}$ of the apples: $12 \div 3 = 4$, $4 \times 2 = 8$ apples.
Alex and Ilya took a total of $3 + 8 = 11$ apples.
So the number left = $12 - 11 = 1$.

PAGE 19 — PERCENTAGES, FRACTIONS AND DECIMALS

1. C
There are 8 triangles in this shape and 2 are shaded in, so that's $\frac{2}{8}$. You can simplify this to $\frac{1}{4}$. $\frac{1}{4}$ is equal to 25%.

2. B
Reading off the chart, 20% of children chose pink as their favourite colour. 20% of 90 is the same as $\frac{2}{10}$ of 90. $90 \div 10 = 9$.
$9 \times 2 = 18$.

3. A
A — 25% of 4 is the same as $\frac{1}{4}$ of 4. $4 \div 4 = 1$. $1 \times 1 = 1$
B — $\frac{3}{4}$ of 8. $8 \div 4 = 2$. $2 \times 3 = 6$.
C — $\frac{2}{5}$ of 10. $10 \div 5 = 2$. $2 \times 2 = 4$.
D — 10% of 25 is the same as $\frac{1}{10}$ of 25.
$25 \div 10 = 2.5$. $2.5 \times 1 = 2.5$
E — $\frac{2}{6}$ of 18. $18 \div 6 = 3$. $3 \times 2 = 6$.

SECTION TWO — WORKING WITH NUMBERS

PAGE 21 — ADDITION

1. B
Round each value to the nearest whole pound.
£13.89 rounds up to £14.00.
£3.35 rounds down to £3.00.
£12.30 rounds down to £12.00.
Add the rounded values together to estimate the answer:
£14.00 + £3.00 + 12.00 = £29.00.
The answer is either B or D. As you rounded down by 65p and up by 11p the estimate is lower than the actual answer. So the actual answer must be B — £29.54.
(You could also use a written method for this question.)

2.   48.43 seconds

Add the four numbers together using the column method:

```
  1 2 . 3 7
  1 1 . 8 8
  1 3 . 2 4
+ 1 0 . 9 4
  4 8 . 4 3
      2
```

Their total time for the race was 48.43 seconds.

PAGE 23 — SUBTRACTION

1.   E

You need to subtract 48.28 from 75.63.
Partition 48.28 into 40.00, 8.00, 0.20 and 0.08.
75.63 – 40.00 = 35.63
35.63 – 8.00 = 27.63
27.63 – 0.20 = 27.43
27.43 – 0.08 = 27.35

2.   Anita

Use the rounding method to estimate the difference in scores for each person. Round each score to the nearest whole number:
Joe: 62 – 58 = 4%
Holly: 64 – 60 = 4%
Lucille: 63 – 63 = 0%
Anita: 65 – 60 = 5%
(Dave's score decreased between test 1 and test 2, so Dave is not included.) As no one else's score increased by around 5%, Anita is the correct answer.

PAGES 24-25 — MULTIPLYING AND DIVIDING BY 10, 100 AND 1000

Warm-Up Activity
0.063, 0.63, 6.3, 63, 630, 6300

Compare the place value of each of the digits in the numbers to put them in the correct order.

1.   B

Start by working out how many books of tickets were sold.
Divide the number of tickets sold by the number of tickets in a book:
1000 ÷ 10 = 100 books. Then divide the amount of money made by the number of books sold to find the cost of each book:
375 ÷ 100 = £3.75.

2.   0.0042

4.2 ÷ 10 = 0.42. The number that fills in the blank should equal 0.42 when it's multiplied by 100. So, divide 0.42 by 100 to find the missing number. 0.42 ÷ 100 = 0.0042.

PAGE 28 — MULTIPLICATION

1.   27 650

350 is 100 times larger than 3.5. 79 is 10 times larger than 7.9. So, the answer to 350 × 79 will be 1000 (100 × 10) times larger than 27.65. 27.65 × 1000 = 27 650.

2.   D

Estimate the answer by rounding each value to the nearest whole number and then multiplying the rounded values together. 6.9 rounds up to 7, 8.2 rounds down to 8. 8 × 7 = 56, so the answer is around 56. The only realistic option is option D, 56.58.

3.   954

Use written multiplication to find the answer:

```
      5 3
×     1 8
    4 2 4
      2
+   5 3 0
    9 5 4
```

PAGE 31 — DIVISION

1.   2.2

First, convert the decimal into a whole number: 8.8 × 10 = 88. Then do the division: 88 ÷ 4 = 22. Since you multiplied 8.8 by 10 at the beginning, you've got to divide your answer by 10 now. 22 ÷ 10 = 2.2.

2.   11

You need to divide 14.50 by 1.30 — to see how many lots of 1.30 there are in 14.50. Partition 14.50 into numbers that are easier to work with. Find a number that's close to 14.50 and is a multiple of 1.30 — there are 10 lots of 1.30 in 13.00, which leaves you with 1.50 left over (14.50 – 13.00 = 1.50). This is enough to buy 1 more soft toy (1.50 – 1.30 = 0.20). The total number of toys you can buy is 10 + 1 = 11.

3.   C

The answer to 19 200 ÷ 4 will be four times larger than the answer to 19 200 ÷ 16 (because 4 is four times smaller than 16). So, multiply 1200 by 4 to find the answer to 19 200 ÷ 4. 1200 × 4 = 4800.

4.   33

You need to divide 264 by 8. Split 264 into two smaller numbers that are easier to divide — e.g. 64 and 200.
64 ÷ 8 = 8
200 ÷ 8 = 25
Add the answers together to find the final answer:
8 + 25 = 33 levels

PAGES 32-35 — ALGEBRA

Warm-Up Activity
8 × 6 = 48
62 – 19 = 43
8 × 5 = 40
84 ÷ 12 = 7
46 + 27 = 73
34 – 16 = 18

1.   £75

The number of hours is 3 and the cost of the parts is £20.
Put these values into the equation.
C = 25 + 10h + p
C = 25 + 10 × 3 + 20
C = 25 + 30 + 20
C = 75
The cost of the electrician was £75.

2.   E

The numbers in the sequence increase by 5 between each term, so the rule for the sequence will begin 5n. When you multiply any of the terms by 5, you always need to add 1 to get the next number in the sequence. So, the expression for the nth term is 5n + 1.

3.   D

Work out each part of the algebraic expression:
The width of the room is 3 metres.
The length of the room is 4 × 3 = 12 metres
(4 times the width).
The height of the room is y metres.
To calculate the volume, multiply the width, length and
height together:
Volume = 3 × 12 × y = 36y

SECTION THREE — NUMBER PROBLEMS

PAGE 37 — MIXED CALCULATIONS

1.   D

The calculations show the prices of all the items rounded up to the
nearest 10p. The only part that's different about all of the options is
the number of pence added or subtracted from the end. Work out how
many pence have been added to each of the prices to round them up.
Orange = 39p, which is rounded to 40p by adding 1p.
3 oranges are bought, so 3p is added to the total.
Carrot cake = £1.99, which is rounded to £2 by adding 1p.
2 carrot cakes are bought, so 2p is added to the total.
Tuna roll = 99p, which has been rounded to £1 by adding 1p.
1 tuna roll is bought, so 1p is added to the total.
Work out how many pence have been added in total.
3p + 2p + 1p = 6p. So D is the answer because you'd need to take 6p
away from the total to get the right amount.

2.   B

Don't forget BODMAS — for all the calculations, you will need to do
the multiplication before the additions and subtractions.
The numbers in the different additions and subtractions range from
12 to 15. The total number added to or subtracted from each
calculation differs by about 5 (e.g. 15 – 13 = 2 and 12 – 15 = -3).
The numbers in the different multiplications also range from 12 to
15, but when multiplied together the results will differ by a greater
amount than the additions and subtractions (e.g. 15 × 13 = 195 and
14 × 13 = 182). So the calculation with the greatest numbers in the
multiplication will give the largest answer.
The largest multiplication is 13 × 15, and two options include this
multiplication. The result of the multiplication will be the same for
both, so just work out which of the two has the greatest number
added to the multiplication:
B — Total added = 14 – 12 = 2
C — Total added = 12 – 13 = -1
B is the answer.

PAGE 41 — WORD PROBLEMS

1.   E

To get 42 tulips, Lena needs to buy 6 bunches of tulips (42 ÷ 7 = 6).
To get 42 roses, Lena needs to buy 7 bunches of roses (42 ÷ 6 = 7).
So 6 × 4.50 = £27, 7 × 3.50 = £24.50. 27 + 24.50 = £51.50

2.   £1.70

You need to work out how much Benni spent.
So £10 – £1.50 = £8.50.
This means that 5 sandwiches cost £8.50, so the cost of
1 sandwich is £8.50 ÷ 5 = £1.70

3.   £17.10

You could work out the profit that Simone makes on each bracelet.
50p – 20p = 30p. Then multiply this by the number she sells. The
easiest thing to do here is to round the number she sells (57) up to
an easier number (60), then do the multiplication. 30 × 60 can be
worked out by finding 3 × 6 = 18, then add on the two zeros to give
1800p, or £18.00. Because you rounded the number sold up by
three, you just need to subtract the cost of 3 bracelets
(3 × 30p = 90p) from £18.00 to give you the answer.
£18.00 – 90p = £17.10.

SECTION FOUR — DATA HANDLING

PAGE 43 — DATA TABLES

1.   B

The number of children who own more than 15 DVDs is shown
by the frequencies in the bottom two rows of the table.
Find the total number of children by adding these frequencies
together: 13 + 6 = 19.

2.   £6

First find the total amount spent on senior citizen tickets by
subtracting the cost of the adult tickets, child tickets and the
booking fee from the "Amount to pay".
£212.50 – £2.50 – £32 – £160 = £18.
The table shows that three senior citizen tickets were bought, so
divide £18 by 3 to find the cost of one ticket: £18 ÷ 3 = £6

PAGE 47 — DISPLAYING DATA

1.   36

You know that 20° = 2 children, so 10° = 1 child. The whole pie chart
is 360° and 360° ÷ 10 = 36, so there are 36 children in the class.

PAGE 49 — MODE, MEDIAN, MEAN AND RANGE

1.   B

Work out the mean, mode, median and range for the
data set you're given.
Mean = (22 + 23 + 17 + 17 + 26) ÷ 5 = 105 ÷ 5 = 21.
Mode = most common value = 17
The number of tea bags listed from smallest to largest:
17 17 22 23 26
Median = middle value = 22
Range = 26 – 17 = 9
Compare your values to the options — B is the correct option.

PAGES 50-51 — MISLEADING DATA

Warm-Up Activity

The article claims that sprouts are more popular with girls than boys, but the data shows that the same proportion of boys and girls like sprouts.

The article says that 75% of boys don't like sprouts so that means
that 100 – 75 = 25% of boys do like them. 25% is the same as
¼, so an equal proportion of boys and girls like sprouts. The article
is misleading because it claims that sprouts are more popular with
girls than boys.

1. C

The headline suggests that sales of pencils have fallen by a massive amount. If you read the graph, the sales have only actually fallen from 500 million to 498 million. The graph makes it look like the sales have fallen more sharply because the axis doesn't start at zero — the drop isn't actually very big compared to the overall number of pencils sold.

PAGE 53 — PROBABILITY

1. C

Go through the options and see if they're true:
A — There is a total of 6 + 3 = 9 in the 'Girl' circle, and only 2 + 5 = 7 outside the girl circle — there are more girls than boys, so not an even chance.
B — There are 2 + 3 = 5 glasses wearers, and 6 + 3 + 2 + 5 = 16 children in total. 5 isn't one quarter of 16, so this statement isn't true.
C — Boy glasses-wearers are shown in the 'Glasses-wearer' circle, but outside of the 'Girl' circle. There are 2 of them, which is a fraction of $\frac{2}{16}$. If you divide both the numerator and denominator by 2, this simplifies to one-eighth. So this statement is true.
D — There are 3 + 2 = 5 glasses-wearers out of 16, so there is less chance that the child selected will be a glasses-wearer than not.
E — There are 3 girls who wear glasses (shown by the overlap of the circles). 3 out of 16 isn't equal to 50%.

SECTION FIVE — SHAPE AND SPACE

PAGE 55 — ANGLES

1. D

Angle c is smaller than a right angle, so it is less than 90°. This means that it must be either 10° or 45°. You can tell that it is about half of the size of a right angle, so the correct answer is option D — 45°.

2. 135°

The total size of the angles on the circular compass is 360°. There are 8 compass points, so the size of the angle between each point is 360 ÷ 8 = 45°. South is three points away from north east so the size of the angle between them is 45 × 3 = 135°.

PAGE 59 — 2D SHAPES

1. C

A scalene triangle has no right angles, no equal angles and no equal sides, so this is the shape that Rhona is describing. All of the other options are incorrect.

2. A

First, rule out the shapes that can't go in that row. A square, an equilateral triangle and a rhombus have all equal side lengths, so you can rule out B, D and E. Next, rule out the shapes that can't go in that column. A rectangle has all equal angles, so you can rule out C. The answer must be A — a trapezium.

3. Isosceles triangle

The shape has no obtuse angles, so all the angles inside the shape must be 90° or less — this means the shape can only be a square, a rectangle or a triangle. The next clue says that it has no right angles, so it can't be a square or a rectangle — it must be a triangle.

The final clue says that two of its sides are equal in length. A right-angled triangle or an isosceles triangle can have two equal side lengths, but this shape doesn't have any right angles. The shape is an isosceles triangle.

PAGE 63 — 2D SHAPES – AREA AND PERIMETER

1. 7.5 cm

The perimeter of the shape is made up of 10 equal length sides. The length of each side is 75 ÷ 10 = 7.5 cm. So, side Z is 7.5 cm.

2. C

Split the shape into two rectangles as shown in the diagram. Work out the length of the missing sides on the smaller rectangle. The horizontal side is 13 – 5 – 5 = 3 cm and the vertical side is 8 – 4 = 4 cm.

Then work out the area of each rectangle. The smaller rectangle is 3 × 4 = 12 cm². The larger rectangle is 13 × 4 = 52 cm². The total area of the shape is 52 + 12 = 64 cm² — option C is correct.

PAGE 65 — SYMMETRY

1. A

The shape is a trapezium.
The diagram shows the reflected shape.

2. 5

The star has 5 lines of symmetry. These are shown on the diagram.

PAGE 69 — 3D SHAPES

1. B

Option B is the only net that will not fold up to make a cube — two of its faces would overlap. The diagram below shows which faces would overlap if you folded it up.

2. 64

The number of vegetable stock cubes that will fit along the length of the box is 4 cm ÷ 1 cm = 4. The number that will fit along the width of the box is 8 cm ÷ 1 cm = 8. The number that will fit up the height of the box is 2 cm ÷ 1 cm = 2. The total number of cubes is 4 × 8 × 2 = 64 vegetable stock cubes.

3. Cuboid

The net has 4 rectangular faces in a line, then 2 squares at the top and bottom — it will fold up to make a cuboid. (A cuboid can also be called a rectangular prism.)

PAGE 71 — SHAPE PROBLEMS

1. C

When you look at the logo from the back of the window it will be flipped over, so you need to look for the option that's a reflection of the original logo. Option C is a reflection of the original logo.

PAGE 75 — COORDINATES

1. D

Go through the options one by one. Imagine plotting each of the points on the grid. A parallelogram is a shape with two pairs of equal length, parallel sides, a pair of equal obtuse angles and a pair of equal acute angles. Only the coordinates for option D make a parallelogram with the existing points on the grid.

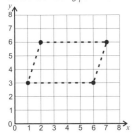

2. (5, 3)

The diagram shows the shape after it has been rotated 90° anticlockwise about the point (6, 7). The coordinates of corner Y are now (5, 3).

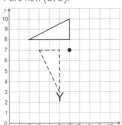

SECTION SIX — UNITS AND MEASURES

PAGE 78 — UNITS

1. D

0.3 g, 3 g and 30 g are all very light — less than the weight of an empty schoolbag, so the answer can't be any of these options.
30 kg is very heavy — about the weight of a child, so this can't be the answer either. The answer must be 3 kg — this is about the weight of 3 bags of sugar, which could easily be carried.

2. 71 servings

There is originally 28.75 litres = 28 750 ml of soup (28.75 × 1000). 350 ml is spilt, so there is 28 750 – 350 = 28 400 ml left.

Now you need to divide 28 400 ml by 400 ml to find the number of servings. To simplify the calculation, you could divide both numbers by 100: 28400 ÷ 400 = 284 ÷ 4.

Now use a written method to do the division:

3. A

Each stride is 50 cm so 2 strides will cover 2 × 50 cm = 100 cm. There are 100 cm in 1 m, so Ben takes 2 strides to walk 1 m. There are 1000 m in 1 km, so in 10 km there are 10 × 1000 = 10 000 m. So to walk 10 000 m Ben must take 10 000 × 2 = 20 000 strides.

PAGE 81 — TIME

1. Max

The youngest child must have the latest date of birth. Children born in 2009 must be younger than those born in 2008, so it can't be Jim or Geeta. October is later in 2009 than March and May, so Max must be younger than Meg and Fred.

2. February

Keep adding the number of pages Kerry completes each month until you reach 154.
Sep = 30
Sep + Oct = 30 + 31 = 61
Sep + Oct + Nov = 61 + 30 = 91
Sep + Oct + Nov + Dec = 91 + 31 = 122
Sep + Oct + Nov + Dec + Jan = 122 + 31 = 153
There are 153 days between September and the end of January, so she will finish her 154-page book in February.

3. D

Work out the time difference in stages like this:

	7 mins		2 hours		15 mins	
4.53 pm	→	5 pm	→	7 pm	→	7.15 pm

Total = 7 mins + 2 hours + 15 mins = 2 hours 22 minutes
Watch out — this isn't the same as 2.22 hours.
2.22 hours is 2 hours and 22 hundredths of an hour.

SECTION SEVEN — MIXED PROBLEMS

PAGES 82-85 — MIXED PROBLEMS

Warm-Up Activity

10% of 40 = ¼ of 16
10 % of 40 = 40 ÷ 10 = 4, ¼ of 16 = 16 ÷ 4 = 4
5^2 – 10 = 3 × 5
5^2 – 10 = 25 – 10 = 15, 3 × 5 = 15
(5 + 3) × 7 = 30 + 26
(5 + 3) × 7 = 8 × 7 = 56, 30 + 26 = 56
0.73 × 100 = 54 + 19
0.73 × 100 = 73, 54 + 19 = 73

1. £40

Work out the volume of the swimming pool.
10 × 10 × 1.6 = 160 m³.
If it costs 25p to fill 1 m³ then it will cost £1 to fill 4 m³.
160 ÷ 4 = 40, so it will cost £40 in total.

2. B

The pie chart is a circle so all of the angles add up to 360°. A section that is 90° would cover ¼ (or 25%) of the pie chart (360 ÷ 4 = 90°). The section for red flowers covers 45° which is half of 90°. So as a percentage, 45° is 25% ÷ 2 = 12.5%. The correct answer is option B.

Index